THE TECHNICAL COLLEGE SERIES

General Editor : W. E. FISHER, o.b.e., d.sc.

*(Formerly Principal, Wolverhampton and Staffordshire
College of Technology)*

MECHANICAL
ENGINEERING SCIENCE

VOLUME I

THE TECHNICAL COLLEGE SERIES

General Editor: W. E. FISHER, O.B.E., D.Sc.

(Formerly Principal, Wolverhampton and Staffordshire College of Technology)

A Selection of the Books in this Series:

NATIONAL CERTIFICATE MATHEMATICS
(In three volumes)
P. ABBOTT, B.A.,
C. E. KERRIDGE, B.Sc.,
H. MARSHALL, B.Sc.,
G. E. MAHON, B.Sc.

EXAMPLES IN PRACTICAL MATHEMATICS FOR
NATIONAL CERTIFICATE
C. C. T. BAKER, B.Sc.

MECHANICAL ENGINEERING
SCIENCE FOR NATIONAL CERTIFICATE
(In two volumes)
J. D. WALKER, B.Sc.(ENG.), A.M.I.MECH.E.

ELECTRO-TECHNOLOGY FOR NATIONAL
CERTIFICATE
Volume I
H. TEASDALE, B.Sc., M.ED., A.M.I.P.E.,
E. C. WALTON, B.ENG., PH.D., M.I.E.E.
Volume II
H. BUCKINGHAM, M.Sc., PH.D.,
E. M. PRICE, M.Sc.

WORKSHOP ENGINEERING
CALCULATIONS AND TECHNICAL SCIENCE
(In two volumes)
J. T. STONEY, B.Sc.

ADVANCED NATIONAL CERTIFICATE MATHEMATICS
(Volumes I and II)
J. PEDOE, M.A.(CANTAB.), B.Sc.(LOND.)

NATIONAL CERTIFICATE WORKSHOP TECHNOLOGY
by T. NUTTALL, A. M.I.MECH.E., A.M.I.P.E.

THE TECHNICAL COLLEGE SERIES

MECHANICAL ENGINEERING SCIENCE

FOR

NATIONAL CERTIFICATE

BY

J. D. WALKER

B.Sc.(Eng.), A.M.I.Mech.E.

Head of the Department of Civil and Mechanical Engineering, Huddersfield College of Technology

VOLUME I

FIRST YEAR

MECHANICS AND HEAT

THE ENGLISH UNIVERSITIES PRESS LTD.

102 NEWGATE STREET

LONDON, E.C.1

FIRST EDITION 1948
SECOND IMPRESSION 1951
THIRD IMPRESSION 1953
FOURTH IMPRESSION 1954
FIFTH IMPRESSION 1958

PRINTED AND BOUND IN ENGLAND BY
HAZELL WATSON AND VINEY LTD
AYLESBURY AND SLOUGH

GENERAL EDITOR'S FOREWORD

THE Technical College Series today includes many books which are outstanding in their particular fields, and it is the aim of the publishers to maintain and develop the worthy tradition of the Series while meeting in full the increasing needs of technical and scientific education.

An outstanding contribution of the technical colleges to education has been the system of National Certificates under which the Ministry of Education and the colleges work in association with leading professional institutions. The system has progressed from its early pre-occupation with engineering until the schemes now cover practically the whole field of higher technology and applied science. The major engineering institutions, the Royal Institute of Chemistry, the Institute of Physics, the Institution of Metallurgists are all associated with National Certificate schemes. There are National Certificates in Building and in Commerce, with each of which a group of professional institutions is associated. Though the pattern of National Certificate Courses was originally dictated by the needs and limitations of the evening student, the system of endorsements obtainable by further study has now brought about the result that these courses have been extended to meet the full requirements of practice in the subjects with which they deal. During recent years the system of part-time-day release of apprentices and learners has become common in all branches of industry as well as in the public services. This has effected something like a revolution in technical education ; and in particular the treatment of National Certificate studies up to the standard already indicated has become much broader.

The books included in the Series will be planned to suit the requirements of three main groups : (i) the part-time and full-time students working in technical colleges for professional qualifications and university degrees, (ii) technologists, managers, and research workers in industry, (iii) teachers in technical colleges and elsewhere who require text-books of high standard, but broad enough in treatment of their subjects to be readily adaptable to local approved schemes of study.

W. E. FISHER.

PREFACE

THIS book is intended to cover the requirements of students taking mechanical or electrical engineering courses in a Technical College. This first volume is planned to correspond to Mechanical Engineering Science work usually done in the first year of the Ordinary National Certificate in both Mechanical and Electrical Engineering. It will be appreciated that the extent of the syllabus for the first year course varies from College to College. Consequently some of the matters included in this volume may be found to fall within the second year syllabus of a particular College. In such a case it is anticipated that the student will be guided by the teacher as to the relevant portion of the book for his requirements. This volume covers the mechanical engineering portion of the syllabus for the first year examination in Mechanical Engineering Science conducted by the Union of Lancashire and Cheshire Institutes, the Union of Educational Institutions and the Northern Counties Technical Examinations Council. The needs of the Junior Technical School student in his Second Year Course have also been in mind in the preparation of this work.

Far too many first year students make their weekly appearance in class without having made any intermediate reference to any textbook. The solution, or otherwise, of the problem set for homework is considered adequate work additional to class work. The result of such an attitude is patent in later years when it is realised that the early fundamentals have not been appreciated. The author's considered opinion is that the student whose ability is to make the most progress and whose stability is to be the most reliable is the one who will make fullest possible use of the textbook to implement the class work instruction given by the teacher.

To present the fundamental principles of mechanical engineering science in a manner acceptable to the young student ; to furnish the young student with a liberal quantity of worked-out examples, including graphical solutions ; to supply the young student with a number of exercises for his own working ; these are the aims which the author has had predominantly in mind during the preparation of this work.

The author would like to place on record his grateful acknowledgment of the valuable help given to him by the Publishers and the Editor Emeritus, Mr. P. Abbott. Also to the Union of Lancashire and Cheshire Institutes, the Union of Educational Institutions and the Northern Counties Technical Examinations Council for permission to use questions which have appeared in their respective Examinations. The Tables at the end of the book are taken from Mr. P. Abbott's Mathematical Tables and Formulæ, by courtesy of the Publishers, Messrs. Longmans, Green & Co. Ltd. Finally the author has pleasure in expressing his indebtedness to his brother Mr. P. Walker for his great help in checking examples.

Crosland Moor.   J. D. WALKER.

CONTENTS

CONTENTS

CHAPTER I

A WORD TO THE BEGINNER

This book has been written to help you in your studies of a grand Science—Mechanical Engineering. A science which finds its way into all activities of life, because we are living in the Machine Age, even though we are on the verge of the Atomic Age. Our food, our clothes, our transport, our entertainments, our public services such as gas, water and electricity are all associated with machines and processes which rely for their correct working and functioning upon the fundamental principles of Mechanical Engineering Science. The speed of the Coronation Scot, the strength of the Sydney Bridge, the dependability of the Austin are all assured as a result of the application of these varied principles. It is the object of this and the succeeding books to introduce you to these basic ideas so that you may be able to take your place with that fine company of people . . . the Engineers.

Of course, you must not expect to start immediately designing bridges or jet propelled aircraft or steam turbines. But you are going to start by being told about the principles upon which such designs are based. In the early stages we can discuss only beams resting on supports ; but unless we are absolutely familiar with these simple ideas we shall not be able to understand and follow the involved calculations required before a bridge like the Menai Straits suspension bridge could be rebuilt. This leads to the reason for writing this chapter.

There have been many students who have started in the first year class. As they have advanced from year to year some have found the work becoming more and more difficult and in many cases they have fallen out by the wayside. Their difficulties have arisen not because the work was becoming more advanced, but because they did not fully grasp and understand the ideas which were given to them in the first year. They thought the first year did not matter. I want you to understand thoroughly now, at the commencement of your course, that the first year is just as important (if not more so) as the years which follow. Your certificates and degrees, which are awarded on the re sults of examinations which you will take some years hence, tend to make you think that it is these later years which are the more important. Think of it like this : as you read these words you do not have to spell out each letter separately or refer to a dictionary for its meaning. If this had to be done for every word, what progress would be made ? On the other hand, because a sound foundation was laid some years ago in this matter of reading you can read straight through this chapter without difficulty. In precisely the same way, if you determine now to grasp fully every principle which is put to you in the first year course, you will avoid many difficulties which would arise in your later courses. The finest way of grasping any principle is to **work out plenty of examples** which are dependent upon that principle. Not just one example which may be set for homework, but a whole series of them. The time which you spend in doing this will be amply rewarded. Don't say, " Oh! I've done all this before." If it is true, it will do you no harm to do it again.

One last word.

Make sure your work is always neat ; whether lecture notes, laboratory work or homework.

Let your **diagrams be Engineering Drawings,** using all the ideas which are given to you in your Drawing Classes. Use a slide rule as soon as you can. It is as essential a part of the Engineer's stock in trade as the file or the pair of compasses.

Determine that you will finish this course as enthusiastically as you have begun it. The Arabs have a proverb, " What one fool can do, another can." The proverb has a good many implications.

So much, then, for the " pep talk."

Now let us discuss forces.

CHAPTER 2

FORCES

Force

Force is generally defined as that which changes, or tends to change, the state of rest or uniform motion of a body.

This definition puts into scientific language some facts with which we are very familiar. We know, for example, that a piece of steel resting on a table will remain in that position until a force is applied to it to cause it to move. If the steel is bolted down to the table, then the force may not be strong enough to move the steel. But it will try to move it. It will tend to move it.

We are, perhaps, not as familiar with the fact that once the force has caused the steel to move, then it will continue to move in the same direction until a second force is applied to it. This force will either alter the direction in which the steel is moving, or it will alter its speed, making it go either faster or slower. Thus the effect of the application of the second force is to change the state of uniform motion of the steel.

Kinds of Force

The force causing the movement in the first case may have a variety of forms. The following are the most usual:

Direct Forces.—Pull applied by a cord attached to the steel. Push applied by a rigid bar attached to the steel.

Attractive Forces.—Force exerted by magnet. Under certain conditions this may be a repulsive force. Force exerted by the earth. This is called the **force of gravity.**

Explosive Forces.—Force exerted by explosion of petrol vapour. Force exerted on bullet by explosion of chemicals.

Characteristics of Force

In order to completely describe a force the following particulars must be known:

Magnitude.—4 lb. or 5 tons.
Direction.—60° to the horizontal or due north.
Sense.—Push or pull.
Point of application.

Graphical Representation of Force

All the above characteristics can be represented graphically if we draw a line whose length to some scale represents the **magnitude** of the force. The **direction** of the line is drawn parallel to the direction of the

3

force. The **sense** of the force can be indicated by an **arrow** drawn on the line. This line is called a **vector**.

Example 1.—*Represent the following forces acting at one point:*

(*a*) 30 lb. in direction due north.
(*b*) 20 lb. in direction due west.
(*c*) 15 lb. in direction south-west.
(*d*) 40 lb. in direction 30° west of north.
Forces (*a*) and (*c*) are pulling away from the point.
Forces (*b*) and (*d*) are pushing towards the point.

The scale chosen is 1 in. = 20 lb.

(*a*) Draw a line in the north direction from point P. Length of line is to represent 30 lb. to the above scale, i.e., length = 1½ in. The arrow will point away from P because the force is pulling away from P.

(*b*) Draw a line in the west direction. Length = 1 in. to represent 20 lb. Since the force is pushing towards P the arrow will point towards P.

(*c*) Draw a line in the south-west direction. This makes 45° with the last line. Length = ¾ in. to represent 15 lb. Arrow points away from P. Force is pulling at P.

(*d*) Draw a line making 30° with the north direction on the west side of the north. Length = 2 in. to represent 40 lb. Arrow points towards P. Force is pushing towards P.

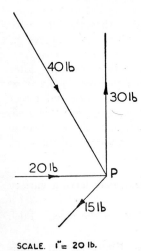

SCALE. 1"= 20 lb.

FIG. 1 — GRAPHICAL RE-
PRESENTATION OF FORCES

The four lines which have now been drawn are four vectors showing the way in which the forces are spaced out. Such a diagram is called a **SPACE DIAGRAM**.

Addition of Forces

Fig. 2 (*a*) shows two forces acting at a point P. 4 lb. pulling towards the right and 3 lb. pulling towards the left. The effect of these two forces on the point P is just the same as that of a single force of 1 lb. acting towards the right. Therefore if P were free to move, it would move towards the right as though it were pulled by a 1 lb. force.

In Fig. 2 (*b*) the 3 lb. force has moved through 180° so that both forces now act in the same direction, i.e., towards the right. The two forces have been shown slightly out of line to make the diagram clearer. Now it is obvious in this case that the effect of these two forces on the point P is the same as that which would be produced by a single force of 7 lb.

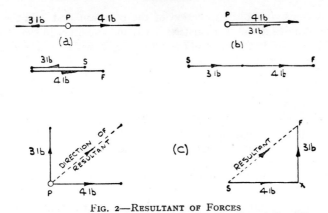

FIG. 2—RESULTANT OF FORCES

The 4 lb. force is fixed in direction while the direction of the 3 lb. force changes. In (a) their directions are opposed and the resultant force is 1 lb. to the right. In (b) they are pulling together giving a resultant force of 7 lb. to the right. In (c) the forces are acting at right angles to each other. Their resultant is found by drawing the vector triangle.

acting towards the right. So that if P were free to move, it would move towards the right as though it were pulled by a 7 lb. force.

This single force which will produce the same effect as the original forces is called their **RESULTANT**.

Definition.—The resultant of a number of forces is that force which will replace the forces and produce the same effect.

When the forces are all acting in the same line the resultant can easily be found by calculation. If the forces are all acting in the same direction, e.g., all towards the right, then the resultant force will act in the same direction and its magnitude will be equal to the ordinary arithmetical sum of the magnitudes of the forces.

Thus in the case (b) Magnitude equals 3 + 4 = 7 lb.

If some of the forces act in opposite directions then we can find the sum of the forces acting towards the right, and the sum acting towards the left. Then the magnitude of the resultant force will be equal to the ordinary arithmetical difference of the magnitudes of the forces acting towards the right and towards the left. The direction of the resultant will depend upon which side has the greatest sum of forces.

In case (a) Magnitude of resultant equals 4 − 3 = 1 lb.

Direction of resultant is towards the right because the sum of the forces acting towards the right are greater than the sum of those acting towards the left.

Now the problem which we have to solve is how to find the resultant of forces which do not act in the same line. For example: What will be the resultant of the 3 lb. and 4 lb. forces if their directions are at 90° to each other as in Fig. 2 (c).

Let us think about the direction of the resultant first. If the point P is free to move it will be clear that it will move neither in the direction of the 4 lb. nor in the direction of the 3 lb. force. It will move in a direction somewhere between these two.

Since the two forces are neither wholly opposing nor wholly assisting each other it may be expected that the magnitude of the resultant will be between 1 lb. and 7 lb.

The following method to find the resultant force can be applied in all cases. It is illustrated in Fig. 2 (c).

(1) Draw the space diagram. This need not be done to scale although the directions of the forces should be correct.

(2) Starting from the point S draw the vector Sx to represent one of the forces.

(3) From the point x draw a vector to represent the next force.

(4) This procedure is repeated until all the forces have been dealt with. The end of the last vector is called F.

(5) Draw a line from the start S to the finish F. This line represents in magnitude and direction the resultant force.

In case (a) SF equals 1 lb. to the right.

(b) SF equals 7 lb. to the right.

(c) SF equals 5 lb. inclined at 37° approximately to the horizontal.

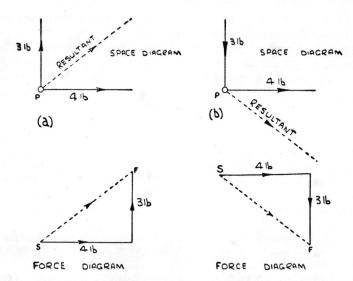

FIG. 3—EFFECT OF SENSE ON RESULTANT

In both (a) and (b) the direction of the 3 lb. force is the same. In (a) its sense is away from P while in (b) its sense is towards P. The resultant is different in the two cases. Notice that the arrows of the *given forces* in the force diagrams follow round in the same direction.

IMPORTANT NOTE.—*The direction of the resultant is always from the start S to the finish F.*

Starting from S the arrows all point in the forward direction until the point F is reached.

The arrow on the vector always points the same way as the arrow shown on the force in the space diagram.

The second diagram to be drawn is called a **FORCE DIAGRAM.**

The importance of having the arrows pointing in the same forward direction is illustrated in the example in Fig. 3. In the first case (*a*) both forces are pulling away from P while in the second case (*b*) the 3 lb. force is pushing towards P. Notice how this difference affects the force diagram and the resultant force. This difference is again illustrated in Examples 2 and 3, page 9.

Equilibrium

A body is said to be in equilibrium when it is completely at rest.

Equilibrant

We have seen in the example in Fig. 2 that the point P would move in the direction of the resultant and therefore it is not in equilibrium. If another force were applied whose magnitude and direction were the same as the resultant except that the sense was opposite, i.e., the new force was pushing towards P, then the point P would be brought to rest. It would be in equilibrium.

Definition.—**The equilibrant of a number of forces is that force which must be added to the forces in order to produce equilibrium.**

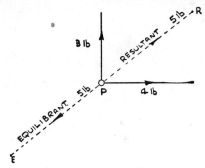

FIG. 4—RESULTANT AND EQUILIBRANT

The equilibrant is always equal in magnitude but opposite in direction to the resultant. The equilibrant is the force which must be added to produce equilibrium.

Considering the 3 lb. and 4 lb. forces acting at the point P (Fig. 4), the resultant of these forces is 5 lb. represented by PR. The equilibrant whose magnitude is the same as the resultant, i.e., 5 lb., must act in the opposite direction as shown by PE.

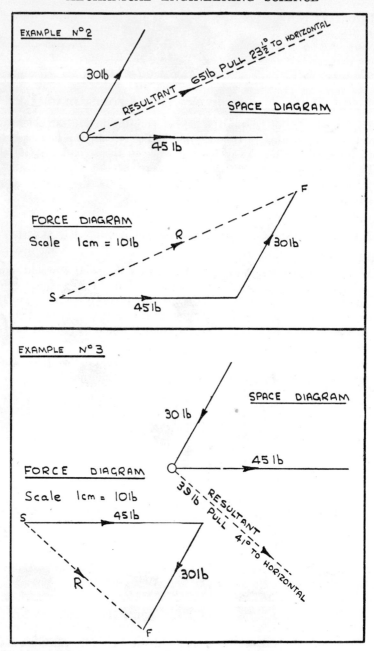

EXAMPLE N° 2

30lb

RESULTANT 65lb PULL 23½° TO HORIZONTAL

SPACE DIAGRAM

45 lb

FORCE DIAGRAM

Scale 1cm = 10lb

F

R

30lb

S

45lb

EXAMPLE N° 3

30 lb

SPACE DIAGRAM

45 lb

FORCE DIAGRAM

Scale 1cm = 10lb

S

45lb

39lb RESULTANT PULL 41° TO HORIZONTAL

R

30lb

F

Fig. 5

Example 2.—*Find the resultant of two forces* (1) 45 *lb. pull acting in a horizontal direction and* (2) 30 *lb. pull acting at an angle of* 60° *to the horizontal.*

(1) Draw the space diagram with the forces shown at the correct angles. The lines representing the forces need not be drawn to scale.

(2) Choose a suitable scale for the force diagram and starting at the point S draw, to scale, the line representing the 45 lb. force.

(3) From the end of this line draw, to scale, a line representing the 30 lb. force, taking care that the arrow is in the same direction as in the space diagram and that the arrows are pointing " forward " in both the 45 and 30 lb. cases.

(4) Join SF. This line represents in magnitude and direction the resultant of the two forces. *Note that the arrow giving the direction points from S to F.*

(5) Draw the dotted line on the space diagram parallel to the line SF on the force diagram. This will indicate the position of the resultant relative to the other two forces. Measure the angle which the resultant makes with the horizontal.

Example 3.—*Find the resultant of two forces* (1) 45 *lb. pull acting in a horizontal direction and* (2) 30 *lb. push acting at an angle of* 60° *to the horizontal direction of the first force.*

The method of procedure is the same as in the above case.

Note.—In both these cases the resultant is actually represented by the diagonal of the parallelogram formed by the two lines representing the two forces. This will always be the case when dealing with TWO forces.

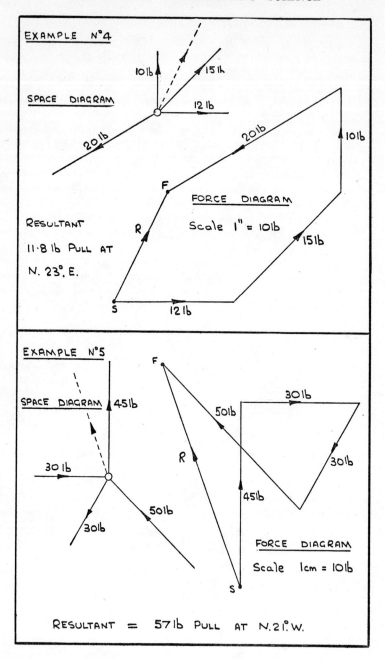

FIG. 6

Example 4.—*Find the resultant of the following forces :*

12 lb. pull due east.

15 lb. pull north-east.

10 lb. pull due north.

20 lb. pull south 60° west.

(1) Draw the space diagram with the forces shown at the correct angles. The lines need not be drawn to scale.

(2) Choose a suitable scale for the force diagram and starting from the point S draw, to scale, the line representing the 12 lb. force.

(3) From the end of this line draw, to scale, a line representing the 15 lb. force, taking care that the arrow is in the same direction as in the space diagram and that the arrows are pointing in the same " forward " direction in both the 12 and 15 lb. cases.

(4) Continue with the other forces in turn drawing each vector at the end of the previous one and in all cases watching the direction of the arrows. Call the end of the last vector to be drawn F.

(5) Join SF. This line represents in magnitude and direction the resultant of the forces. *Note that the arrow giving the direction points from S to F.*

(6) Draw the dotted line on the space diagram parallel to the line SF on the force diagram. This will indicate the position of the resultant relative to the other forces. Measure the angle which the resultant makes with the north direction.

Example 5.—*Find the resultant of the following forces .*

45 lb. pull due north.

30 lb. push due west.

30 lb. pull south 30° west.

50 lb. push south-east.

Proceed as outlined above. Watch particularly the directions in which the 30 lb. and 50 lb. vectors are drawn. Starting from S the arrows must point away from S.

NOTE.—The vectors may cross each other or pass through the junction of two other vectors.

The order in which the vectors are drawn will not affect the result. You may commence with any one and proceed in any order.

Three Forces in Equilibrium

If the force diagram for three forces acting at a point is a closed triangle, there will be no resultant and the forces will be in equilibrium. Conversely, if we know that the forces are in equilibrium then we know that the force diagram will be a triangle whose sides are drawn parallel to the direction of the forces and whose lengths are proportional to the magnitude of the forces.

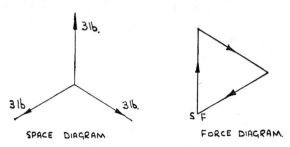

SPACE DIAGRAM   FORCE DIAGRAM.

FIG. 7—FORCES WITH NO RESULTANT
The force diagram for this arrangement of forces is a closed triangle. The points S and F coincide. There is therefore no resultant. The forces are in equilibrium amongst themselves. Hence if we know that three forces are in equilibrium we know that the force diagram will be a triangle.

Triangle of Forces Law. **If three forces acting at a point are in equilibrium, they can be represented by the sides of a triangle drawn parallel to the forces.**

This very important law can be applied to a number of engineering problems particularly in the case where we know the magnitude of one of the forces and require to find the magnitude of the other forces. It is important to notice that all the forces must act in the same plane.

For example, Fig. 8 shows a simple arrangement of a jib crane. The three forces acting are :

　　　　　　　(i) the load,
　　　　　　　(ii) the thrust of the jib,
　　　　　　　(iii) the tension in the tie.

We know the magnitude and direction of force (i) but we know only the direction of the forces (ii) and (iii).

Reactions

If a 7 lb. weight is placed on a horizontal surface, the surface immediately supplies an upward force of 7 lb. to keep the weight in equilibrium. This force is called the **reaction** of the surface. If the weight were now suspended from a hook, the hook would exert an upward force of 7 lb. on the weight. This upward force is called the **reaction** of the hook. It **is** a fundamental law of mechanics that :

Force and reaction are always equal and opposite.

In the case of a *smooth surface the reaction is always at right angles to the surface.*

The three forces acting on the roller in Fig. 9 are :

    (i) the weight of the roller W,
    (ii) the pull up the plane P,
    (iii) the reaction of the plane which is at right angles to the plane R.

The direction of all the forces is known but the magnitude of only force (i) is known. Since the forces are in equilibrium we can determine the magnitude of the other forces by drawing the triangle of forces.

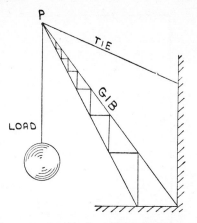

FIG. 8—FORCES IN EQUILIBRIUM
The three forces acting at the point P are in equilibrium. The load is pulling away from P. The jib is thrusting towards P, and the tie is pulling away from P. The three forces can be represented by a triangle drawn with its sides parallel to the direction of the forces.

Bow's Notation

This is a convenient method of lettering the forces for reference purposes.

A capital letter A, B, etc., is placed in each space between two forces. The force is then referred to by the pair of letters in the adjoining spaces, thus force AB. The vector in the force diagram representing the force AB is lettered *ab*. This will apply to all the forces and their corresponding vectors.

A number of miscellaneous examples are worked out in the following pages.

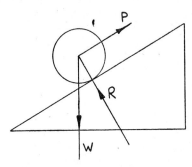

FIG. 9—FORCES IN EQUILIBRIUM
The roller is held in position on the inclined plane by the force P. This force together with the weight of the roller and the reaction of the plane produce equilibrium. The forces can be represented by the triangle of forces.

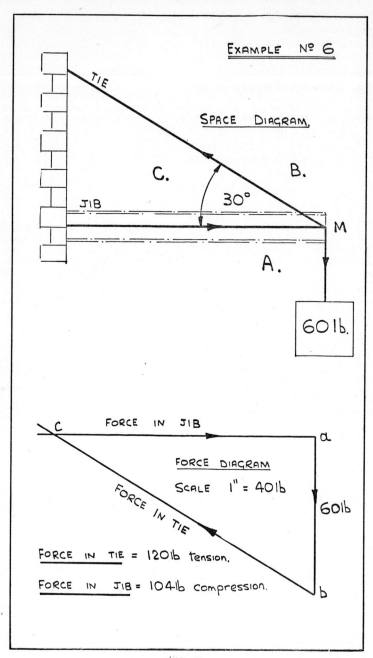

EXAMPLE N° 6

SPACE DIAGRAM,

TIE

C.

B.

JIB

30°

M

A.

60 lb.

FORCE IN JIB

c

a

FORCE DIAGRAM

SCALE 1" = 40 lb

FORCE IN TIE

60 lb

b

FORCE IN TIE = 120 lb tension.

FORCE IN JIB = 104 lb compression.

FIG. 10

Example 6.—Wall Crane. Details are given of a wall crane. Determine the forces in the jib and tie when a load of 60 lb. is suspended as shown.

METHOD.

(1) Draw the space diagram showing the outline of the crane. This need not be drawn to any particular scale, but the directions of the various members must be correct. The essential thing is to obtain the directions of the forces acting at M.

(2) Letter the spaces between the forces, using Bow's Notation. The force in the jib will be referred to as *ca*, the force in the tie as *bc* and the 60 lb. load as *ab*.

(3) Choose a suitable scale for the force diagram. Draw *ab* parallel to the cord supporting the load. The length of *ab* will represent 60 lb. to the scale of the force diagram.

(4) Through *b* draw a line parallel to the direction of the tie. Through *a* draw a line parallel to the direction of the jib. The intersection of these two lines gives the point *c*.

(5) The length of *bc* represents to scale the force in the jib. The length of *ca* represents to scale the force in the tie.

NOTE.—*The arrows in the force diagram all point the same way round the triangle. They also point in the same direction as those on the corresponding member in the space diagram.*

The jib is always in compression. It exerts a thrust towards the point of suspension. It is usually made from a strong beam or a lattice girder.

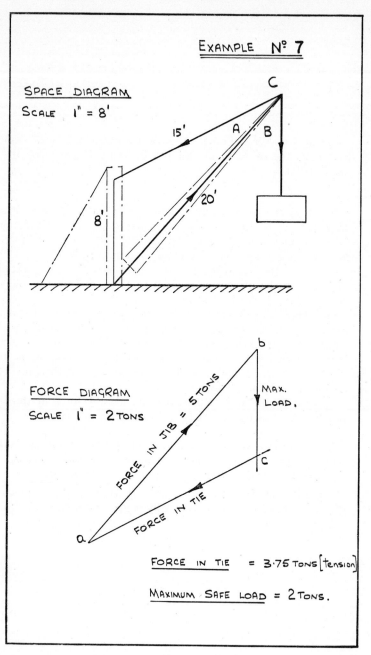

FIG. 11

Example 7.—Jib Crane. In a jib crane the length of the jib is 20 ft. and the tie, which is 15 ft. long, is fastened to a point 8 ft. vertically above the lower end of the jib. If the maximum load which the jib can safely carry is 5 tons, what is the greatest load which the crane can safely lift?

METHOD.

In this case the force whose magnitude and direction are known is that of 5 tons in the jib.

(1) Draw the space diagram to scale showing the outline of the crane. The lengths of the members are given to enable the direction of the forces to be obtained.

(2) Letter the spaces between the forces, using Bow's Notation. The force in the jib will be *ab*, that in the tie will be *ca*, while the load will be referred to as *bc*.

(3) Choose a suitable scale for the force diagram. Draw *ab* parallel to the direction of the jib. The length of *ab* will represent 5 tons to the scale of the force diagram.

(4) Through *b* draw a line parallel to the direction of the load. Through *a* draw a line parallel to the direction of the tie. The intersection of these lines gives the point *c*.

(5) The length of *bc* represents the load which can be carried by the crane when the force in the jib is 5 tons. It represents the maximum safe load which the crane can carry. The length *ca* represents the tension in the tie when this load is being carried.

Notice the direction of the arrows in both diagrams.

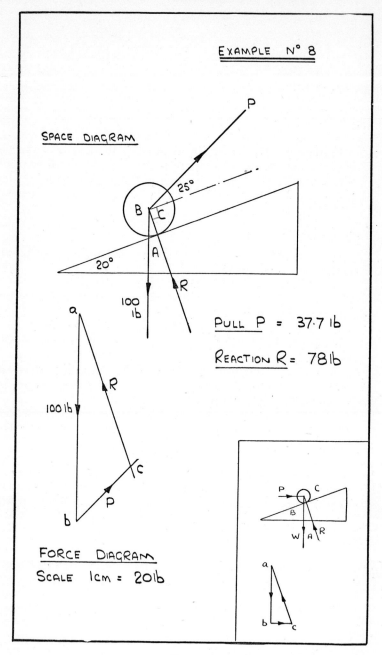

EXAMPLE N° 8

SPACE DIAGRAM

25°

B C

20°   A

100 lb

R

PULL P = 37.7 lb

REACTION R = 78 lb

a

R

100 lb

c

b   P

FORCE DIAGRAM
SCALE 1cm = 20lb

FIG. 12

Example 8.—A roller weighing 100 lb. is being pulled up an inclined plane by a force P which makes an angle of 25° with the plane. The inclination of the plane is 20° to the horizontal. Determine the magnitude of the pull and also the reaction of the plane.

METHOD.

The three forces acting on the roller are ·
　　　　(i) its weight 100 lb.,
　　　　(ii) the pull P,
　　　　(iii) the reaction of the plane which is at right
　　　　　　angles to the plane.

(1) Draw the space diagram to show the direction of these forces. This diagram need not be drawn to any particular scale since the angles are given.

(2) Letter the spaces between the forces, using Bow's Notation. The weight will be *ab*, the reaction *ca*, and the pull *bc*.

(3) Choose a suitable scale for the force diagram. Draw *ab* parallel to the direction of the weight. The length of *ab* will represent 100 lb. to the scale of the force diagram.

(4) Through *b* draw a line parallel to the direction of the pull P. Through *a* draw a line parallel to the direction of the reaction, i.e., at right angles to the plane. The intersection of these lines gives the point *c*.

(5) The length of *bc* represents the pull P. The length of *ca* represents the magnitude of the reaction.

The smaller diagram shows the construction for the case where the pull (or push) is horizontal. Direction of the reaction is still the same.

NOTE. —**The angle between the reaction and the weight is always equal to the inclination of the plane** *provided the plane is smooth.*

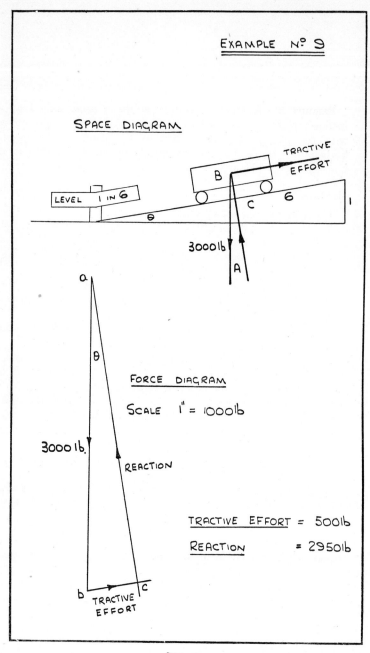

FIG. 13

Example 9.—Determine the force necessary to move a truck weighing 3000 lb. up an incline of 1 in 6 at constant speed. The force is acting parallel to the plane.

METHOD.

This is a similar case to Example 8. In all problems dealing with trains moving up inclines, cars and lorries moving up hills, the tractive effort or the force producing motion is always parallel to the plane.

(1) Draw the space diagram to show the direction of the forces. The expression 1 in 6 means that for every 6 ft. moved *along the track* the truck is 1 ft. higher than it was originally.

(2) Using Bow's Notation letter the spaces between the forces. The weight will be *ab*, the tractive effort *bc* and the reaction of the rails or the plane will be *ca*.

(3) Choose a suitable scale for the force diagram. Draw *ab* vertically, i.e., parallel to the direction of the weight. The length of *ab* will represent 3000 lb. to the scale of the force diagram.

(4) Through *b* draw a line parallel to the direction of the tractive effort, i.e., parallel to the plane. Through *c* draw a line parallel to the reaction of the plane, i.e., at right angles to the plane. The intersection of these lines gives the point *c*.

(5) The length of *bc* represents the magnitude of the tractive effort. The length of *ca* represents the magnitude of the reaction of the plane.

NOTE.—The angle between the weight and the reaction is equal to the inclination of the plane.

Since the tractive effort is parallel to, and the reaction at right angles to the plane, the angle between the lines *bc* and *ca* is 90°. This is always the case when the pull is parallel to the plane.

From the triangle *abc* we have

$$\text{Tractive effort} = \text{weight} \times \sin \theta$$
$$= \text{weight} \times \tfrac{1}{6}$$

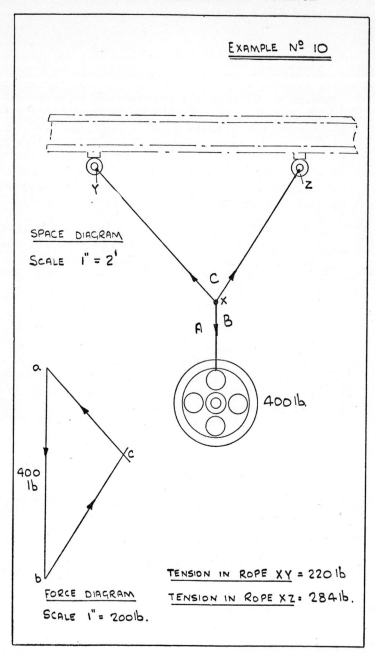

EXAMPLE Nº 10

SPACE DIAGRAM

SCALE 1" = 2'

400 lb.

400 lb

FORCE DIAGRAM

SCALE 1" = 200 lb.

TENSION IN ROPE XY = 220 lb

TENSION IN ROPE XZ = 284 lb.

FIG. 14

Example 10.—A casting weighing 400 lb. is supported by two ropes fastened to eyebolts 4 ft. apart. The lengths of the ropes are $3\frac{1}{2}$ ft. and 3 ft. Determine the forces in the ropes.

METHOD.

(1) Draw the space diagram to scale to show the direction of the ropes and therefore of the forces acting at the point X.

(2) Using Bow's Notation letter the spaces between the forces. The weight of the casting will be represented by *ab*, the force in the rope XY by *ca* and that in the rope XZ by *bc*.

(3) Choose a suitable scale for the force diagram. Draw *ab* vertically, i.e., parallel to the direction of the weight of the casting. The length of *ab* will represent 400 lb. to the scale of the force diagram.

(4) Draw through *b* a line parallel to the rope XZ. Through *a* draw a line parallel to the rope XY. The intersection gives the point *c*.

(5) The length of *bc* represents the magnitude of the force in rope XZ. The length of *ca* represents the magnitude of the force in rope XY. Both ropes are subject to tension.

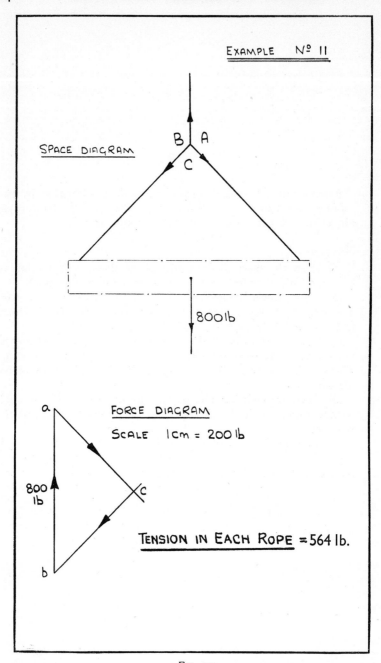

EXAMPLE   N⁰ 11

SPACE DIAGRAM

800 lb

FORCE DIAGRAM

SCALE   1 cm = 200 lb

800 lb

TENSION IN EACH ROPE = 564 lb.

FIG. 15

Example 11.—A shaft weighs 800 lb. A crane lifts the shaft by means of a rope sling and each half of the sling makes an angle of 45° with the shaft. Determine the force in each half of the sling.

METHOD.

The force in the vertical chain which is carrying the sling will be equal to the weight of the shaft. We have therefore three forces meeting at a point. The directions are all known. The magnitude of one of the forces is 800 lb. upwards.

(1) Draw the space diagram to show the direction of the forces. Since the angles are given, this diagram need not be drawn to any particular scale.

(2) Letter the spaces between the forces, using Bow's Notation. The upward pull in the crane chain will be *ba* and the forces in the ropes of the sling *ac* and *cb*.

(3) Choose a suitable scale for the force diagram. Draw *ba* vertically upwards, i.e., parallel to the pull in the chain. The length of *ba* will represent 800 lb. to the scale of the force diagram.

(4) Through *b* draw line parallel to the direction of the left hand rope. Through *a* draw line parallel to the direction of the right hand rope. Intersection of these lines gives the point *c*.

(5) The length of *cb* represents the magnitude of the force in the left hand rope. The length of *ac* represents the magnitude of the force in the right hand rope.

Resolution of Forces

Resolving, or splitting, a force into two parts or components is the reverse operation to that of finding the resultant of two forces. Observing the effect of the two components is very often a helpful method of determining the effect of the force. For example, consider the effect which

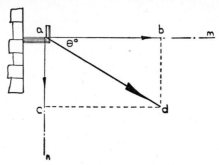

FIG. 16—RESOLUTION OF FORCES

The force *ad* pulling on the hook produces two effects : (i) Direct pulling of the hook out of the wall. (ii) Bending the hook downwards. These two effects are caused by the horizontal and the vertical components of the original force.

the inclined force of 10 lb. will have upon the wall hook. It will tend to bend the hook at the same time as it tends to pull it out of the wall.

The vertical component *ac* is the component tending to bend the hook.

The horizontal component **ab** is the component tending to pull the nail out of the wall.

The magnitude of these two components can be found either graphically or mathematically.

Graphical Method.—Given the magnitude and direction of the force to find its components in two given directions *an* and *am*

       (i) Draw the vector *ad* to represent the force.

       (ii) Draw *db* parallel to *an*.

       (iii) Draw *dc* parallel to *am*

ab and *ac* represent the two components of the force *ad*. The magnitude of the components can be found by measuring the lengths *ab* and *ac* using the same scale as was used in drawing the vector *ad*.

We are generally told the directions in which the components lie, these two directions being usually, though not necessarily, at right angles to each other.

Mathematical Solution

If the force makes an angle θ with one of the given directions, assumed to be at right angles to each other, then the magnitude of the components can be calculated as follows :

Horizontal component $ab = ad \cos \theta$
Vertical   component $ac = ad \sin \theta$

Two other familiar examples are illustrated in Figs. 17 and 18.

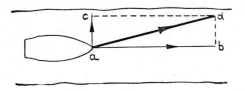

FIG. 17—RESOLUTION OF FORCES
The ab component of the force ad pulls the barge along the canal.
The ac component tends to turn the barge into the left bank.

The barge is moved along the canal by means of a rope which is inclined to the direction of the centre line of the barge. The force is therefore tending to turn the barge into the bank, an effect which must be counteracted by the rudder.

The turning effect is produced by component ac.

The forward pulling effect is produced by component ab.

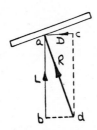

FIG. 18—RESOLUTION OF FORCES
The normal force R of a wind stream against an inclined surface has two components: a lift component L tending to lift the surface; a drag component D causing motion to the left. It is the lift component which is responsible for the performance of aircraft.

The effect of a wind stream on an inclined plate such as an aircraft wing can be studied by resolving into component parts.

The normal force R (that is the force acting at right angles to the surface) has two components:

(i) ab which tends to lift the plate,
(ii) ac which tends to cause the plate to drag.

It is the lift component which is so very important in aircraft performance.

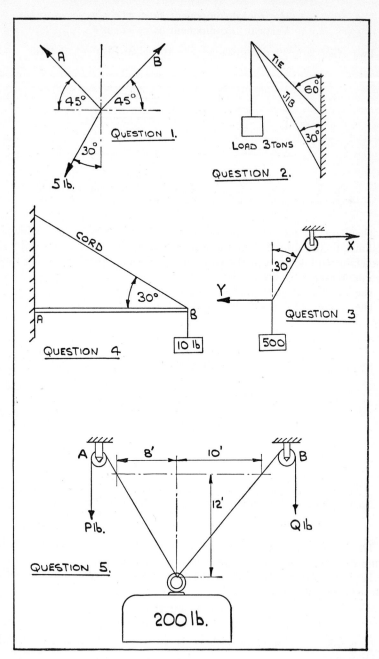

FIG. 19

EXERCISE 1.

The diagrams for Questions 1 to 5 are given in Fig. 19.

(1) Three forces acting at a point in the directions shown are in equilibrium. It is known that one of the forces has a magnitude of 5 lb. Determine the magnitude of the other two forces.

(2) Find the force in the jib and tie when a load of 3 tons is hung from the crane shown in the diagram.

(3) A casting weighing 500 lb. is hung from a chain which passes over a smooth pulley. What will be the magnitude of a horizontal force applied at Y to pull the chain through an angle of 30° from the vertical? What is the force in X?

(4) A rod AB, whose weight may be neglected, is hinged at A and held horizontally by a cord as shown. Determine the thrust in the rod.

(5) A casting weighing 200 lb. is being lifted by two ropes passing over pulleys A and B as shown. Determine the pulls P and Q assuming that the pulleys are frictionless. (This means that the pull P in the vertical portion of the rope will be the same as that in the inclined portion of the same rope. Similarly for Q.)

(6) A roller weighing 50 lb. is being pulled up a plane inclined at 30° to the horizontal by a rope which makes 20° with the plane (upwards). Find the force in the rope and the reaction between the roller and the plane. If the rope will break under a load of 60 lb. what will be the greatest **additional** load which can be placed on the roller?

(7) A machine 3 tons in weight is supported by two chains attached to the same point on the machine ; one of these chains goes to an eye bolt in the wall and is inclined at 30° to the horizontal ; the other goes to a hook in the ceiling and is inclined at 45° to the horizontal. Find the tensions in the chains.

(8) The following forces act at a point :
 16 lb. in direction due east,
 20 lb. in direction due north,
 30 lb. in direction north-west,
 12 lb. in direction 30° south of west.
Find the magnitude and direction of the resultant.
 All the forces are pulling away from the point.

(9) A barge is being towed along a canal by a rope inclined at 15° to the direction of the canal. The tension in the rope is 200 lb. Find the force moving the barge along the canal and the force pulling it towards the bank. If another tow rope attached to the same point on the barge makes 25° with the direction of the canal but is fastened to a horse on the opposite bank to the first, what will now be the force moving the barge along the canal and the force pulling it towards the bank? The tension in the second rope is 150 lb.

(10) Two tugs are towing a liner by means of cables. One tug induces a pull of 100 tons in its cable in a direction due east and the other induces a pull of 150 tons in a direction 45° north of east. Determine the resultant pull on the liner in magnitude and direction.

(11) The following forces act at a point :

    (a) 30 lb. in direction due north.

    (b) 20 lb. in direction due west.

    (c) 15 lb. in direction south-west.

    (d) 10 lb. in direction 30° west of north.

Forces (a) and (c) are pulling away from the point.

    (b) and (d) are pushing towards the point.

Find the magnitude and direction of the resultant.

(12) In a simple jib crane the jib is inclined at an angle of 60° to the horizontal and the tie rod at an angle of 45° (upwards). A load of 8 tons is suspended from the crane head. Determine the forces in the jib and tie rod.

(13) In a simple jib crane the vertical crane post is 8 ft. high, the jib is 13 ft. long and the tie is 7 ft. long. Find the forces in jib and tie rod when a weight of $2\frac{1}{2}$ tons is supported at the crane head.

(14) The resultant thrust on the foundations of a dam is 450 tons at an angle of 25° to the vertical. Find the force tending to make the foundation slide. If the maximum sliding force which the dam can resist is 250 tons, what will be the maximum resultant force, at the above angle, which the foundation will stand ?

(15) State what is meant by the resolution of forces and show how to resolve a force in two directions at right angles to one another. A weight suspended by a cord is pulled by a horizontal force so that the cord is inclined to the vertical. Find the angle of inclination if the tension in the cord is double the weight. N.C.T.E.C.

(16) A weight of 30 lb. is suspended by two cords, 4 ft. and 6 ft. long, respectively, from two points at the same level and 8 ft. apart. Find the tension in each cord. N.C.T.E.C.

(17) Describe an experiment to verify the triangle of forces. A pendulum consists of a bob weighing 4 oz. carried at the end of a cord. If the horizontal force is applied to the bob so that the cord makes an angle of 30° with the vertical, find the magnitude of the force and the tension on the cord. N.C.T.E.C.

(18) A body is in equilibrium under the action of three coplanar forces. State the conditions which the forces must fulfil.

A weight of 5 lb. is supported by cords of lengths 4 ft. and 5 ft. respectively, attached to points in the same horizontal plane and 6 ft. apart. Find the tension in the cords. N.C.T.E.C.

(19) The pressure on the piston of a certain petrol engine when the crank has travelled 20° beyond top dead centre and is on the working stroke is 240 lb. per sq. in. The cylinder bore is $3\frac{1}{2}$ in., the stroke length

is 4 in., and the connecting rod is 7 in. long. Determine the force along the axis of the connecting rod and hence the turning moment on the crankshaft at this instant. **N.C.T.E.C.**

(20) State the principle of the triangle of forces.

Three members of a pin jointed frame meet at a point. One of the members is vertical and connected to the other two at its lower end. The second and third members make angles of 120° and 210° respectively with the vertical member, the angles being measured in a clockwise direction from it. If the force in the vertical member is 10 tons compressive, find the magnitude and nature of the forces in the other two members. **U.L.C.I.**

(21) Two forces OA and OB of 5 lb. and 7 lb. respectively, pull on a body at a point O, the angle AOB being 70°. Find the magnitude and the direction of a third force which will balance these two. **U.L.C.I.**

(22) A carriage mounted on wheels which may be assumed to be frictionless rests on a plane inclined at 30° to the horizontal. If the carriage weighs 8 lb., find by graphical construction the force required to keep it in equilibrium :

(a) when the force is applied horizontally,
(b) when the force is applied in a direction parallel to the plane. **U.L.C.I.**

(23) A weight of 12 lb. is suspended from the junction of two strings 25 in. and 15 in. long respectively. The two strings are attached to two points A and B, 30 in. apart. AB is horizontal.

(a) By drawing diagrams to scale, find the tensions in the strings.
(b) State the general effect on the tensions in the strings if A and B are moved further apart. **U.E.I.**

(24) Explain what is meant by the " equilibrant " of a number of forces. A shaft weighs 1 ton. A crane lifts the shaft by means of a rope sling and each half of the sling makes an angle of 50° with the shaft. By calculation or by measurement, find the force in each half of the sling. **U.E.I.**

(25) A weight of 40 lb. is held in equilibrium on a smooth inclined plane by a force X parallel to the plane. The angle the plane makes with the horizontal is 25°.

Find by measurement or calculation, the force X and the reaction of the plane. **U.E.I.**

(26) Three forces, A, B, and C in the same plane, meet at a point D. A, of magnitude 5 lb., acts in a direction north-west, B, of magnitude 4 lb., in a direction due east, and C, of magnitude 3 lb., in a direction due south.

(a) Is the point D in equilibrium ?
(b) If not, what alteration in magnitude and direction must be made to C in order that D may remain in equilibrium ? **U.E.I.**

(27) A body weighing 20 lb. rests on a plane inclined at 30° to the horizontal. Neglecting friction, find graphically the force which will maintain equilibrium when :

(a) it acts horizontally,

(b) it acts upwards at 45° to the horizontal.

NOTE.—The two angles are measured anticlockwise from the horizontal.

U.E.I.

(28) What do you understand by the triangle of forces ? A cylinder cover, weighing 3 cwt., has eye bolts fitted on a diameter 4 ft. 6 in. apart and equidistant from the centre. It is slung by two chains each 6 ft. long, from a hook, each chain being attached to an eye bolt. Find, graphically, the pull in each chain.

U.E.I.

(29) The piston of a horizontal steam-engine is 12 in. in diameter and the piston rod is $1\frac{1}{2}$ in. in diameter. The effective steam pressure on the piston rod side of the piston is 100 lb. per sq. in., calculate the total pull in the piston rod. The connecting rod of the engine is 5 ft. long and the crank arm 1 ft. long. Find, by means of a scale drawing, the pull in the connecting rod and the normal reaction between the crosshead and the guide bar when the crank arm is 60° from the inner dead centre, the piston moving away from the crankshaft.

U.E.I.

(30) Two pulling forces acting at a point are applied to a body, one of 50 lb. acting north-east and the other 30 lb. acting 30° west of north. Represent these two forces graphically and find their resultant. Also find graphically the horizontal and vertical components of the resultant force.

U.E.I.

CHAPTER 3

THE TURNING EFFECT OF A FORCE

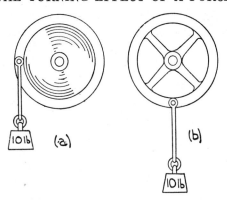

FIG. 20—TURNING EFFECT OF A FORCE
The 10 lb. force will turn the wheel in an anticlockwise direction in (a).
The same force fastened to the same point will not cause rotation in (b).
The turning effect of the force involves both the magnitude of the force
and the distance of the line of action of the force from the turning point.

An arrangement is shown in Fig. 20 in which a weight is fastened
to a point on the rim of a wheel which is free to rotate on a shaft.
Although the same weight is used in each case the turning effect produced
in (a) is much greater than that produced in (b). In fact, if the weight is
fastened to a point immediately below the shaft axis, as shown in (b),
no turning effect is produced. The weight will not turn the wheel.

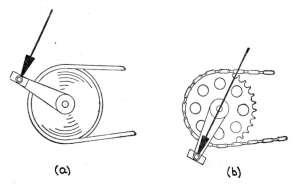

FIG. 21—TURNING EFFECT OF A FORCE
The force applied as in case (a) will be very useful in driving the cycle.
The same force acting in case (b) is useless for driving. The line of action
of the force must not pass through the turning point.

A similar case is shown in Fig. 21. The arrow shows the direction of the force applied by the leg to the crank of a bicycle. In (*a*) the force is producing rotation of the crank, while in (*b*) the same applied force will not produce any rotation.

So we see that the position of the line of action of a force is equally as important as the magnitude of the force, especially when considering turning effects produced by the force. We shall use the expression " moment of a force " to mean the importance of a force in the same way that we use the word " momentous " in the expression " momentous occasion," which means important occasion.

Now the majority of the forces which we shall have to consider will be trying to produce turning or rotation. We shall not always want them to succeed in producing rotation and in many cases it will be part of the engineer's work to design means of adequately preventing rotation. For

FIG. 22—TENDENCY TO TURN

As soon as the engine moves on to the bridge, its weight tries to turn the bridge in an anticlockwise direction about the right hand support. The left hand support immediately provides an upward force called a reaction to prevent this turning. If the left hand support is strong enough it will be able to supply the necessary reaction. If it is not strong enough the weight of the engine will win, the left hand support will collapse and the bridge will turn in an anticlockwise direction.

example, when the engine passes on to the girder bridge, Fig. 22, its own weight acting vertically down is a force which is trying to rotate the bridge about one of its supports. The further the engine moves on to the bridge from the right hand side the greater becomes the tendency to turn the bridge about the right hand support. The bridge is prevented from turning by the action of the left hand support. If the masonry in this support is not strong enough to withstand the turning effect then the support will collapse and the bridge will turn in an anticlockwise direction about the right hand supporting column. It is equally as true to think of the weight of the engine trying to turn the bridge in a clockwise direction about the left hand support and to think of the strength of the masonry in the right hand support withstanding this turning effect.

The turning effect or the moment of a force will thus play a very important part in many of the calculations which the engineer has to make.

The moment of a force about a point is a measure of the turning effect which it produces about the point. Its value is given by the product of the magnitude of the force and the perpendicular distance of the line of action of the force from the point. The force P in fig. 23 is acting along

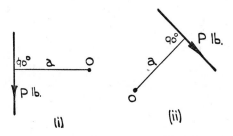

FIG. 23—CLOCKWISE AND ANTICLOCKWISE MOMENTS
Force P produces an anticlockwise turning effect about O in case (i) and a clockwise turning effect in case (ii). The magnitude of the turning effect is the same in each case. It is measured by the product of the force P and the shortest distance or the perpendicular distance of the line of action of P from O. In each case the moment of P about O is P*a*.

a line whose perpendicular distance from the point O is *a*. The moment of the force about A is therefore given by P*a*. In (i) the force is providing an anticlockwise moment while in (ii) it is providing a clockwise moment. In all cases when we are dealing with the moment of a force we shall have to determine, either by calculation or by measuring, the length of a line drawn from the point to the line of action of the force. The line which we draw must **always be perpendicular to the direction of the force,** that is it must always cut the force line at 90°. It will therefore be the shortest line which can be drawn from the point to the line of action of the force.

Definition.—**The moment of a force about a point is equal to the product of the magnitude of the force and the perpendicular distance between the point and the line of action of the force.**

The unit in which we shall usually measure the moment of a force is the pound-foot (lb. ft.). Two alternatives which are used are the pound-inch (lb. in.) and the ton-foot (ton ft.). Choice of units will depend upon the measurements which are given. Thus if the force P in Fig. 23 is 20 lb. and the distance *a* is 3 ft. then the moment of P about O will be 20 × 3 = 60 lb ft   Or if the force is 2 tons and the distance 5 ft. then the moment about O will be 2 × 5 = 10 ton ft.

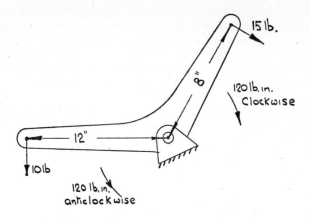

Fig. 24—Principle of Moments
The bell crank lever is in equilibrium under the action of two turning
moments. An anticlockwise moment due to the 10 lb. force and a clockwise
moment due to the 15 lb. force. These two moments must be equal in
magnitude if the lever is not to turn.

Principle of Moments

The bell crank lever shown in Fig. 24 is free to turn on its fulcrum or
pivot. A 15 lb. force is applied as shown in a direction at right angles
to the arm of the lever. The turning moment produced by the force
about the pivot is $15 \times 8 = 120$ lb. in. in a clockwise direction. Unless
some other moment is applied to the lever it will immediately proceed
to rotate in a clockwise direction about the pivot. Suppose that another
weight of 10 lb. is hung at the end of the horizontal arm. Then since
the line of action of the force due to the weight is vertical the perpendicular distance from the fulcrum will be 12 in. and the moment of
the force about O will be $10 \times 12 = 120$ lb. in. in an anticlockwise direction. The tendency to turn the lever in a clockwise direction is just
balanced by the tendency to turn it in an anticlockwise direction. The
lever will remain stationary ; it will be in equilibrium under the action
of the two forces. We can derive a very important principle from these
observations. If the clockwise and the anticlockwise moments are equal
then the lever will be in equilibrium. Reversing the conclusion we can
say that if the lever is in equilibrium under the action of a number of
forces then the clockwise moments about any point are equal to the
anticlockwise moments. This is known as the principle of moments.

Definition.—The principle of moments states that if a body is in equilibrium under the action of a number of forces then the clockwise moments
about any point must equal the anticlockwise moments about the same
point.

It is very important to notice that in all problems of this type we measure the **PERPENDICULAR** distance of the line of action of the force from the fulcrum.

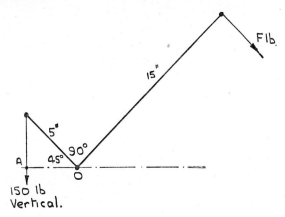

FIG. 25

Example 12.—Thus in determining the force F in Fig. 25 required to overcome the 150 lb. load, the anticlockwise moment of this load about O is 150 × OA. We must therefore either measure or calculate this length OA.

Taking moments about O.

Clockwise moments   = 15F
Anticlockwise moments = 150 × OA lb. in.
$$= 150 × 3·53 \text{ lb. in.}$$
$$15F = 150 × 3·53$$
$$F = 35·3 \text{ lb.}$$ N.C.T.E.C.

Example 13.—A light rod AB 20 in. long is pivoted at A and hangs vertically. Forces are applied simultaneously by means of strings attached to the rod. A force CD of 4 lb. is applied at C, 16 in. below A. CD is horizontal and D is to the left of the rod. A horizontal force BE of 3 lb. is applied at B, E being to the right of the rod. Find the resultant turning moment on the rod. Where must a horizontal force of 2 lb. be applied to prevent rotation of the rod ?

Neglecting the weight of the rod there are three forces acting on the rod.

(i) Force CD   4 lb.
(ii) Force BE   3 lb.
(iii) Reaction at pivot R lb

Take moments about the pivot A.

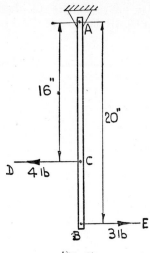

FIG. 26

Force CD : perp. distance of CD from A = 16 in.

∴ moment of CD about A = 16 × 4

= 64 lb. in. clockwise.

Force BE : perp. distance of BE from A = 20 in.

∴ moment of BE about A = 20 × 3

= 60 lb. in. anticlock-

wise.

Reaction R : Since this force acts at the pivot it has no moment
about the pivot.

Resultant moment = 64—60

= 4 lb. in. clockwise.

i.e., lever will turn about A in a clockwise direction.

In order to hold it in equilibrium an anticlockwise moment of
4 lb. in. must be applied.

i.e., a horizontal force of 2 lb. must be applied on the same
side of the lever as the 3 lb. force and at a distance of

$\dfrac{4}{2}$ = 2 in. from the pivot. This force will then provide

the balancing anticlockwise moment of 2 × 2 = 4 lb. in.

Example 14.—A light rod AB 20 in. long is pivoted at A and
hangs vertically.   Forces are applied simultaneously by means
of strings attached to the rod.   A force CD of 4 lb. is applied at
C, 16 in. below A, the angle BCD being 45°, D being to the left
of the rod, and a horizontal force BE of 3 lb. is applied at B, E
being to the right of the rod.   Find the resultant turning moment

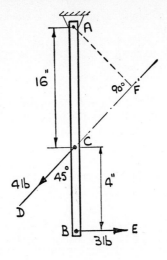

FIG. 27

on the rod. Where must a force of 2 lb. be applied to prevent rotation of the rod? U.E.I.

Take moments about the pivot A.

Force CD:
  Perpendicular distance of CD from A = AF.
  This distance AF can be found by measurement from a scale drawing.
  Alternatively it can be found by calculation.
  Angle CAF is 45°.
  AC is 16 in.

  Since angle AFC is 90° we can say $\dfrac{AF}{AC} = \cos CAF$

$$= \cos 45°$$
$$\therefore AF = AC \cos 45°$$
$$= 16 \times 0.7071$$
$$= 11.31 \text{ in.}$$

  Moment of CD about A = 4 × 11.31
  $$= 45.24 \text{ lb. in. clockwise.}$$

Force BE:
  Perpendicular distance of BE from A = 20 in.
  Moment of CD about A = 3 × 20
  $$= 60 \text{ lb. in. anticlockwise.}$$

  Resultant moment = 60 − 45.24
  $$= 14.76 \text{ lb. in. anticlockwise.}$$

  i.e., lever will turn in anticlockwise direction.

To hold it in equilibrium apply a clockwise turning moment of 14·76 lb. in.

i.e., apply force of 2 lb. at $\dfrac{14·76}{2} = 7·38$ in. from A on the same side of the lever as force CD.

Example 15.—Draw a line, horizontally, 5 in. long. Mark it AE. On it mark off AB, BC, and CD, 2 in., 1 in., and ½ in. respectively. AE is a lever pivoted at C. Vertical forces of 2, 3, 4, and 4 lb. act at A, B, D, and E, respectively. State what will happen to the lever under the action of these forces and why? What additional force will be required at A to produce equilibrium? Neglect the weight of the lever.   U.E.I.

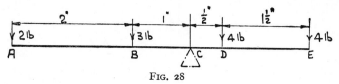

FIG. 28

By calculation the distance DE is 1½ in.

Take moments about the pivot C.

Clockwise moments :

Force at D. Moment about C = 4 × ½ = 2 lb. in.
Force at E. Moment about C = 4 × 2 = 8 lb. in.

Total clockwise moments = 10 lb. in.

Anticlockwise moments :

Force at A. Moment about C = 2 × 3 = 6 lb. in.
Force at B. Moment about C = 3 × 1 = 3 lb. in.

Total anticlockwise moment = 9 lb. in.

Resultant moment on lever = 10 − 9
= 1 lb. in. clockwise.

The lever will rotate in a clockwise direction about the pivot. Lever can be balanced by applying an anticlockwise moment of 1 lb. in.

i.e., by applying a force of ⅓ lb. at A which is 3 in. from C. Moment of additional force = ⅓ × 3 = 1 lb. in.

Example 16.—In a certain lever safety valve the distance from the hinge to the weight suspension point is 15 in., and from the hinge to the centre line of the valve 2·5 in. The effective diameter of the valve is 2 in. If the valve is just to lift when the pressure is 250 lb. per sq. in., what must be the load on the arm? Neglect the weight of the valve and the arm. What resulting force is then acting on the hinge?

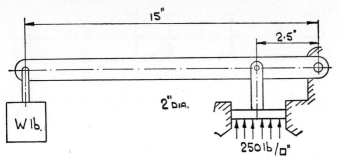

FIG. 29

Upward thrust on valve V = area × pressure

$$= \frac{\pi}{4}2^2 \times 250$$

$$= 785 \text{ lb.}$$

Let W lb. = load on the arm.

Take moments about hinge O.

Clockwise moment due to up thrust = $785 \times 2\frac{1}{2}$ lb. in.

Anticlockwise moment due to load = $W \times 15$ lb. in.

Since lever is in equilibrium these two moments are equal

$$\therefore \quad W \times 15 = 785 \times 2\frac{1}{2}$$

$$W = \frac{785 \times 2\frac{1}{2}}{15}$$

$$= 130\tfrac{5}{6} \text{ lb.} \quad \textbf{Ans.}$$

Force on hinge :

Since the lever is in equilibrium then :

Sum of upward forces = sum of downward forces.

$$785 = 130\tfrac{5}{6} + \text{force exerted by hinge on}$$
lever

$$\therefore \text{ Force on hinge} = 785 - 130\tfrac{5}{6}$$

$$= 654\tfrac{1}{6} \text{ lb.} \quad \textbf{Ans.}$$

NOTE.—This $654\tfrac{1}{6}$ lb. is acting vertically down on the LEVER, i.e., the lever is pushing upwards against the hinge with a force of $654\tfrac{1}{6}$ lb.

Example 17.—A uniform beam AB is loaded as shown. Calculate the reactions at the supports :

(a) Neglecting the weight of the beam.

(b) Taking into account the weight of the beam, which is 0·6 tons.

Let the reaction at A be R_a tons,

and the reaction at B be R_b tons.

(a) Neglecting the weight of the beam.

To find R_b take moments about A.

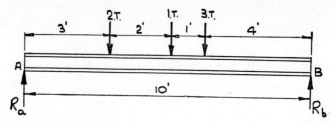

FIG. 30

Clockwise moments $\qquad = (2 \times 3) + (1 \times 5) + (3 \times 6)$ ton ft.

$\qquad = 29$ ton ft.

Anticlockwise moments $= 10R_b$ ton ft.

Equating moments :

$$10R_b = 29$$
$$R_b = 2\cdot9 \text{ tons.}$$

To find R_a take moments about B.

Clockwise moments $\qquad = 10R_a$ ton ft.

Anticlockwise moments $= (3 \times 4) + (1 \times 5) + (2 \times 7)$ ton ft.

$\qquad = 31$ ton ft.

Equating moments :

$$10R_a = 31$$
$$R_a = 3\cdot1 \text{ tons}$$
$$R_b = 2\cdot9 \text{ tons. \textbf{Ans.}}$$

Check : The sum of the upward forces must always equal the sum of the downward forces.

$\quad$ *Upward* $\quad R_a + R_b = 3\cdot1 + 2\cdot9 = 6$ tons

$\quad$ *Downward* $\quad 2 + 1 + 3 \qquad\qquad = 6$ tons.

(b) Taking the weight of the beam into account.

The weight is considered to act at the mid point of the beam. Its moment about A will be $0\cdot6 \times 5 = 3$ ton ft.

Total clockwise moments about A will be $29 + 3 = 32$ ton ft.

Equating moments :

$$10R_b = 32$$
$$R_b = 3\cdot2 \text{ tons.}$$

The anticlockwise moment of the weight about B will be $0\cdot6 \times 5 = 3$ ton ft.

Total anticlockwise moments about B will be $31 + 3 = 34$ ton ft.

Equating moments :

$$10R_a = 34$$
$$R_a = 3\cdot4 \text{ \textbf{tons.}}$$
$$R_b = 3\cdot2 \text{ \textbf{tons. Ans.}}$$

Check :
Upward Forces = Downward Forces.
$3 \cdot 4 + 3 \cdot 2 \quad = 2 + 1 + 3 + 0 \cdot 6$
$6 \cdot 6 \qquad = 6 \cdot 6$

Example 18.—A uniform lever, 20 in. long, weighs 40 lb. It is hinged at A and supported horizontally by a cord CB fastened to B. A weight 100 lb. is hung at D, 5 in. from B. What is the tension in the cord ?

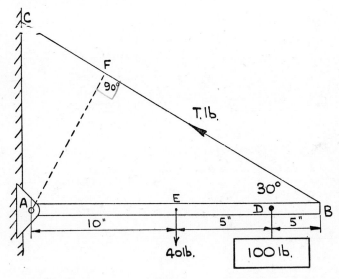

FIG. 31

Let T lb. = tension in cord.
The weight of the lever is taken as acting at E, the mid point
 of its length.
Take moments about A.
Clockwise moments

$= (40 \times AE) + (100 \times AD)$
$= (40 \times 10) + (100 \times 15)$
$= 400 + 1500$
$= 1900$ lb. in.

Anticlockwise moments $= T \times AF$
 AF by measurement is 10 in.
 ∴ anticlockwise moments $= 10T$ lb in.
Equating moments :
$\qquad 10T = 1900$
$\qquad T = 190$ **lb. Ans.**
The tension in the cord is **190 lb.**

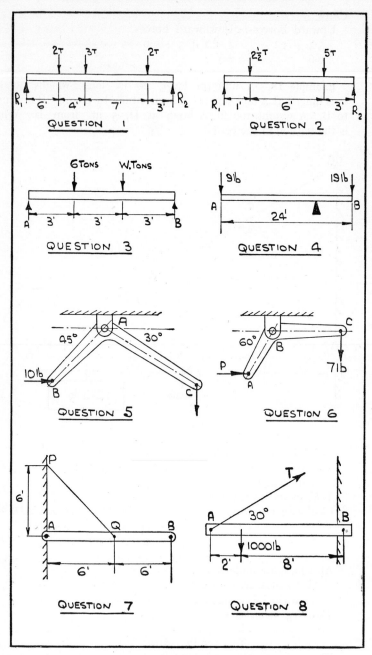

FIG. 32

EXERCISE 2

The diagrams for Questions 1 to 8 are given in Fig. 32.

(1) Calculate the reactions R_1 and R_2 for the beam loaded as shown. Neglect the weight of the beam.

(2) Calculate the reactions R_1 and R_2 for the beam loaded as shown. Neglect the weight of the beam.

(3) The uniform beam shown weighs 1 ton. The reaction at B is 5 tons. Determine the load W and the reaction at A.

(4) The uniform beam AB weighs 2 lb. and carries weights of 9 lb. and 19 lb. at A and B respectively. Determine the position of the support to make the beam balance.

(5) The bell crank lever is pivoted at A. AB is 12 in. and AC is 24 in. What weight must be hung at C to balance a horizontal force P of 10 lb. applied at B ?

(6) The bell crank lever ABC is pivoted at B and carries a weight of 7 lb. at C. Determine the horizontal force P needed to prevent the lever turning. Neglect the weight of the lever. AB = 9 in., BC = 12 in.

(7) The uniform rod AB weighs 2 lb. It is hinged at A and held up by the cord PQ. Determine the pull in the cord.

(8) AB is a uniform arm which weighs 200 lb. and is 10 ft. long. What is the pull in the tie T when a load of 1000 lb. is supported at a point 2 ft. from A ?

(9) A uniform horizontal beam 25 ft. long is supported at the ends and carries the following loads : 2 tons 4 ft. from left hand support, 8 tons 13 ft. from the right hand support, and 6 tons 22 ft. from the left hand support. If the beam weighs 1 ton, calculate the reactions at the supports. If the right hand support is then moved 5 ft. nearer to the left hand support, which remains stationary, what will the new reactions become ?

(10) A lever of weight 9 lb. is 28 in. long. At one end is hung a weight of 6 lb. Find the point about which the lever will rest in equilibrium in a horizontal position.

(11) A uniform beam AB 15 ft. long weighing 100 lb. is supported on two supports, C which is 2 ft. from A, and D which is 3 ft. from B. Loads of 80 lb. and 120 lb. are applied at A and B. Determine the reactions of the supports.

(12) ABC is a wireless mast assumed to be rigid, which has a horizontal pull on it at the top of 300 lb. The mast is kept vertical by a guy-wire attached to the point B, 25 ft. from the base C, this wire making an angle of 35° with the mast. If the mast is 45 ft. long, find the pull in the guy-wire, which is on the opposite side of the mast to the horizontal pull at the top.

(13) State the " principle of moments."

In a certain lever safety valve the distance from the hinge to the weight suspension point is 10 in. and from the hinge to the centre line of the valve 2 in. The effective valve diameter is $1\frac{3}{4}$ in. If the valve is just about to lift when the pressure is 240 lb. per sq. in., what must be the load on the arm? Neglect the weight of the valve and the arm.

N.C.T.E.C.

(14) A uniform horizontal bar AB 4 ft. long rests on a support at A and on another at C 3 ft. from A. If the weight of the bar is 2 lb. calculate the load at B which will just produce no load on support A.

N.C.T.E.C.

(15) A uniform plank 10 ft. long weighing 20 lb. is resting on trestles 8 ft. apart so that one trestle is 1 ft. from one end of the plank. Objects weighing 15 lb., 14 lb., and 8 lb. are placed at points 2 ft., 6 ft., and 9 ft. from one end of the plank. What will be the loads on the two trestles? What principle is used to calculate these loads? State the principle clearly.

N.C.T.E.C.

(16) A uniform beam 16 ft. long and weighing 30 lb. rests on two supports 3 ft. from each end. Find the maximum weight which can be hung at one end without the beam overbalancing.

N.C.T.E.C.

(17) A uniform horizontal beam of weight 200 lb. rests on supports 20 ft. apart. Loads of 2 cwt. and 4 cwt. are placed 5 ft. and 15 ft. respectively from the left hand support. Find the pressure on the supports.

N.C.T.E.C.

(18) Explain what is meant by the moment of a force about a point. A uniform lever AB is 6 ft. long and weighs 10 lb. It is supported by two pegs, one 2 ft. from A and the other 1 ft. from B. A load of 40 lb. is suspended 1 ft. from A and a load of 50 lb. is suspended 2 ft. from B. Calculate the pressure on each peg.

U.E.I.

(19) A horizontal beam AB of uniform section 7 ft. long and weighing 6 lb. is supported at each end by a spring balance. The beam carries concentrated loads of 17 lb., 10 lb., and 20 lb. at distances 1 ft., 3 ft., and 5 ft. respectively from A.

Draw a diagram to scale showing the arrangement and calculate the readings on the spring balances.

U.E.I.

(20) A uniform bar 10 ft. long weighing 2 lb. per foot is supported on knife edges at its ends. Loads of 10 lb., 4 lb., and 16 lb. are placed at distances of 1 ft., 6 ft., and 8 ft. respectively from the left hand support. Find the magnitudes of the reactions at the knife edges.

U.E.I.

(21) In an experiment on parallel forces a uniform beam 40 in. long and weighing 2 lb. was suspended by means of spring balances at the ends A and B. A weight of 5 lb. was suspended at C, 12 in. from the left balance A. The readings of the spring balances were observed to be 4·4 lb. and 2·6 lb. Are these readings correct? If they are incorrect, what is the amount of error in each of the readings?

U.E.I.

(22) The horizontal arm OA of a cranked lever is 12 in. long.   he other arm OB is 8 in. long and the angle between the arms is 135°, B being above OA.   A vertical downward force of 20 lb. acts at A and a horizontal force P acts at B and keeps the lever balanced.   Find the magnitude of the force P, also the magnitude and direction of the reaction at the pivot O.   (All the forces act in the same plane as the lever.)
                                                                      U.E.I.

(23) A horizontal girder weighing 21 lb. per foot length rests on supports 20 ft. apart.   Vertical loads of 1 ton and 2 tons are supported by the girder at points 5 ft. and 14 ft. respectively from the left end. Find the reactions of these supports.   U.L.C.I.

(24) A horizontal beam of uniform section and 18 ft. long rests on supports at its ends.   The beam weighs 540 lb. and carries a load of 2 tons a at point 4 ft. from one end and a load of 1 ton at a point 5 ft. from the other end.   Find the reactions of the supports.   U.L.C.I.

(25) A rod of uniform section 6 ft. long and weighing 20 lb. rests on a fulcrum at one end and is supported in a horizontal position by a vertical force F acting at the other end.   Determine the magnitude of F when the rod also supports a weight of 40 lb. at a point 2 ft. from the fulcrum. Also find the pressure on the fulcrum.   U.L.C.I.

CHAPTER 4

STRESS AND STRAIN

Consider a bar of steel of uniform diameter subjected to a force acting at each end tending to pull the bar apart. Such a force is called a **tensile** force. It produces two important effects.

(1) In trying to pull the bar apart, it creates internal **STRESSES** throughout the whole length of the bar.

(2) It increases the length of the bar, causing a change to take place in its dimensions, thus producing **STRAINS**.

$$\text{Stress is measured by } \frac{\text{force}}{\text{cross section area.}}$$

$$\text{Strain is measured by } \frac{\text{change in length}}{\text{original length.}}$$

Example 19.—A bar 8 in. long, 0·3 sq. in. cross sectional area, is subjected to a tensile force of 1800 lb. and is found to extend to 8·0015 in. Determine the stress in the material and the strain produced.

$$\text{Stress} = \frac{\text{force}}{\text{area}} = \frac{1800}{0·3} = 6000 \text{ lb. per sq. in.} \quad \textbf{Ans.}$$

$$\text{Strain} = \frac{\text{change in length}}{\text{original length}}$$

$$= \frac{8·0015 - 8}{8} = \frac{0·0015}{8}$$

$$= 0·0001875$$

$$= 1·875 \times 10^{-4}. \quad \textbf{Ans.}$$

Notice that STRAIN has no units. It is only a ratio of lengths.

By means of an instrument known as an extensometer it is possible to measure the extension of the bar produced by the application of varying loads. The following results were obtained from an experiment carried out on a bar of steel.

Length of bar   10 in.   Cross sectional area 0·5 sq. in.

Load (lb.)	Extension (thousandths of inch)
0	0
1000	0·66
3000	2·0
5000	3·3
7500	5·0
10,000	6·7
14,000	9·3
18,000	12·0

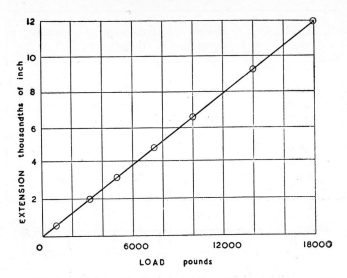

FIG. 33—GRAPH SHOWING EXTENSION OF A BAR SUBJECTED TO AXIAL PULL.

The load-extension graph is a straight line passing through the origin (Fig. 33). *The extension is therefore directly proportional to the applied load.*

This relationship between load and extension will always apply to any elastic material. It can be demonstrated very easily with the use of a spiral spring as shown in Fig. 34. The spring carries a scale pan which can be loaded with weights. The extension of the spring can be measured directly with a metre rule. The graph of load and extension will be very similar to that shown in Fig. 33, except that the loads will be smaller and the extensions will be greater.

Now let us calculate the corresponding stresses and strains produced in the steel bar of the above experiment and draw a graph (Fig. 35) showing the relationship between these values.

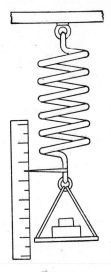

FIG. 34.

Load (lb.)	Stress (lb. per sq. in.)	Extension (thous.)	Strain
0	0	0	0
1000	2000	0·66	0·000066
3000	6000	2·0	0·0002
5000	10,000	3·3	0·00033
7500	15,000	5·0	0·0005
10,000	20,000	6·7	0·00067
14,000	28,000	9·3	0·00093
18,000	36,000	12·0	0·0012

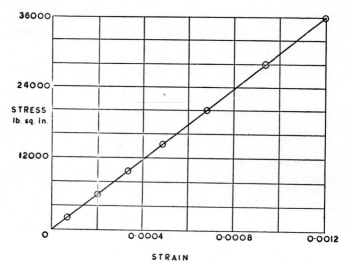

Fig. 35—Stress-strain Graph for the Elastic Range.

This graph illustrates a very important law known as **Hooke's Law,** which deals with the stresses and strains set up in an elastic material. Hooke's Law states :

> **The strain produced in an elastic material is directly proportional to the stress which produces it.**

In other words, $\dfrac{stress}{strain} = constant.$

This constant is called " **Young's Modulus of Elasticity** " and is usually denoted by " E." Some values of E for various materials are given in the following table.

TABLE I.

Material	Young's Modulus (lb. per sq. in.)
Steel	30,000,000
Copper	12,000,000
Brass	10,000,000
Wood	1,400,000

Let W = applied load in pounds (tensile or compressive)
    a = cross section area in sq. in.
    L = length in in.
    x = extension in in.
    E = Young's Modulus in lb. per sq. in.

$$\text{Stress} = \frac{W}{a} \text{ lb. per sq. in.}$$

$$\text{Strain} = \frac{x}{L}$$

$$E = \frac{\text{stress}}{\text{strain}}$$

$$= \frac{\frac{W}{a}}{\frac{x}{L}}$$

$$E = \frac{WL}{ax}$$

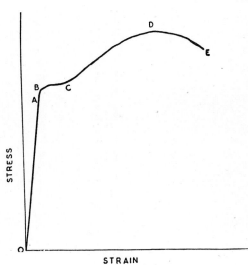

FIG. 36—COMPLETE STRESS-STRAIN GRAPH FOR STEEL.

In the experiment referred to on page 49 the maximum load applied was 18,000 lb., with a corresponding stress of 36,000 lb. per sq. in. If the load had then been gradually increased until the bar broke the complete stress-strain graph would be as shown in Fig. 36. This graph is typical of those obtained from mild steel specimens.

Between O and A, stress is proportional to strain, in fact the portion of the graph from O to A is the same as that show in Fig. 35 drawn to a different scale. The point A is called " the limit of proportionality " or " limit of elasticity," since beyond this point the metal is no longer elastic and stress is no longer proportional to strain. The metal is in the plastic state. When the load is removed the strain will not disappear, as would be the case up to the elastic limit. The metal is now said to have a " permanent set." As the stress is increased a point is reached when the material begins to yield. The specimen extends without increasing the load ; the strain may be increased up to 20 times its previous amount. This is shown by the portion B—C on the graph. The point B at which this occurs is called the " yield point." At C the resistance of the bar increases and additional load is required to produce further extension. There now appears to be a marked change in the texture of the metal, especially near the middle portion of the specimen. The surface which was bright becomes dull. There is also a decrease in the diameter of the central portion ; a " waist " begins to form. Due to this change in cross sectional area, the stress at the waist increases without further increase in the load, in fact the load is reduced and therefore the graph of the stress calculated on the *original* area will be shown as D to E. The load at D is the **maximum load** carried by the specimen. Fracture takes place at the point E.

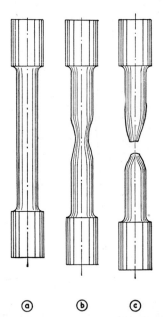

(a)   (b)   (c)

FIG. 37—BEHAVIOUR OF STEEL SPECIMENS IN TENSION
The specimen approximately 8 in. long and 0.75 in. diameter is subjected to an axial pull. As the load increases the specimen increases in length and a " waist " forms as shown at (b). This reduction in cross-sectional area is followed by a reduction in the load but an increase in the actual stress value. Since the stress in Fig. 36 is calculated from load divided by initial cross sectional area the stress-strain curve falls off between D and E. Finally the specimen fractures as shown in (c).

Ultimate Tensile Strength and Factor of Safety

The **Ultimate Tensile Strength** of a metal is an indication of the maximum tensile stress which can be carried by the metal without causing the metal to break.

$$\text{Ultimate Tensile Strength (U.T.S.)} = \frac{\text{maximum load}}{\text{original area}} \text{ lb. per sq. in.}$$

In practice it would be very undesirable to stress any metal beyond the elastic limit. If the load is removed from any part of a machine or structure then that part should return to its original unstressed dimension. This will only happen provided the part has not been stressed beyond the elastic limit. A maximum **Allowable Working Stress** is therefore chosen and designs are based upon this figure. The allowable working stress is a fraction of the ultimate strength of the metal.

$$\text{Allowable Working Stress} = \frac{\text{Ultimate Tensile Strength}}{\text{Factor of Safety.}}$$

Example 20.—A mild steel bar 8 in. long, $\frac{1}{2}$ in. diameter, is subjected to a direct pull of 1 ton. If E for steel is 30×10^6 lb. per sq. in., determine (i) the stress in the steel and (ii) the extension of the bar.

(i) Area of bar $= \dfrac{\pi}{4} \times \left(\dfrac{1}{2}\right)^2 = 0 \cdot 197$ sq. in.

$\quad$ Stress $\quad = \dfrac{\text{load}}{\text{area}} = \dfrac{1 \times 2240}{0 \cdot 197}$

$\quad\quad\quad\quad\quad = 113,80$ **lb. per sq. in. Ans.**

(ii) Strain $\quad = \dfrac{\text{stress}}{\text{E}} = \dfrac{11,380}{30 \times 10^6} = \cdot 000379$

$\quad$ Extension $\quad =$ strain $\times$ length

$\quad\quad\quad\quad\quad = \cdot 000379 \times 8$

$\quad\quad\quad\quad\quad = \cdot 00303$ in. **Ans.**

Example 21.—A mild steel bar, Fig. 38, 12 in. long has a diameter of 1 in. for 8 in. of its length and $\frac{5}{8}$ in. for the remainder. It is subjected to a direct pull of 3 tons. Given that E for steel is 30×10^6 lb. per sq. in., determine (i) the stress in each part of the bar, and (ii) the total extension of the bar.

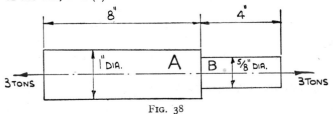

Fig. 38

The load acting on each part of the bar is the same, 3 tons. Consider part A :

Area $\qquad = \dfrac{\pi}{4} \times 1^2 = 0.785$ sq. in.

Stress $\qquad = \dfrac{\text{load}}{\text{area}} = \dfrac{3 \times 2240}{0.785} = 8550$ lb. per sq. in.

Strain in A $\quad = \dfrac{\text{stress}}{E} = \dfrac{8550}{30 \times 10^6} = .000285$

Extension of A $= $ strain $\times$ length

$\qquad\qquad\quad = .000285 \times 8$

$\qquad\qquad\quad = .00228$ in.

Consider part B:

Area $\qquad\qquad = \dfrac{\pi}{4} \times \left(\dfrac{5}{8}\right)^2 = 0.318$ sq. in.

Stress $\qquad = \dfrac{\text{load}}{\text{area}} \qquad = \dfrac{3 \times 2240}{0.318}$

$\qquad\qquad = 21,150$ lb. per sq. in.

Strain in B $\quad = \dfrac{\text{stress}}{E} \quad = \dfrac{21,150}{30 \times 10^6} = .000705$

Extension of B $=$ strain $\times$ original length

$\qquad\qquad\quad = 0.000705 \times 4$

$\qquad\qquad\quad = 0.00282$ in.

Total extension $=$ extension of A $+$ extension of B

$\qquad\qquad\quad = 0.00228 + 0.00282$

$\qquad\qquad\quad = 0.0051$ in.

Stress in A $\qquad = 8550$ lb. per sq. in. $\left.\begin{array}{l}\\ \\ \\ \end{array}\right\}$ Ans.

Stress in B $\qquad = 21,150$ lb. per sq. in.

Total extension $= 0.0051$ in.

Example 22.—A mild steel test piece 0.63 in. diameter and 5 in. gauge length, was subjected to a tensile test until it broke. The extension at various loads was noted and a load-extension graph was drawn. From the graph the extension was found to be 0.0036 in. for a load of 2.68 tons. Determine the value of the modulus of elasticity of the steel.

Area of bar $\quad = \dfrac{\pi}{4} \times 0.63^2 = 0.313$ sq. in.

Stress in bar $\; = \dfrac{\text{load}}{\text{area}} \qquad = \dfrac{2.68}{0.313} = 8.56$ tons per sq. in

Strain $\qquad = \dfrac{\text{extension}}{\text{length}} = \dfrac{0.0036}{5} = 0.00072$

Modulus of elasticity E $\quad = \dfrac{\text{stress}}{\text{strain}}$

$\qquad\qquad\qquad\qquad\; = \dfrac{8.56}{0.00072}$

$\qquad\qquad\qquad\qquad\; = 11,900$ tons per sq. in. **Ans.**

Example 23.—Calculate the diameter of a metal tie rod which is to transmit a pull of 8 tons if the ultimate tensile stress of the metal is 24 tons per sq. in. and the factor of safety is to be 5.

$$\text{Allowable working stress} = \frac{\text{ultimate tensile stress}}{\text{factor of safety}}$$

$$= \frac{24}{5} = 4 \cdot 8 \text{ tons per sq. in.}$$

$$\text{Area of rod} \qquad = \frac{\text{load in tons}}{\text{stress in tons per sq. in.}}$$

$$= \frac{8}{4 \cdot 8}$$

$$= 1 \cdot 67 \text{ sq. in.}$$

$$\text{Diameter of rod} \qquad = \sqrt{\frac{1 \cdot 67 \times 4}{\pi}}$$

$$= 1 \cdot 46 \text{ in. Ans.}$$

EXERCISE 3

(1) A mild steel bar 10 in. long, 0·75 in. diameter, is subjected to a pull of 2 tons. If E for steel is 30×10^6 lb. per sq. in. determine (1) the stress in the steel and (2) the extension in the bar.

(2) A bar of brass has a cross section of 1 in. by 0·8 in. The bar is 20 in. long and is subjected to a direct pull of 0·75 tons. What is the stress in the bar and the extension if the modulus of elasticity for brass is 10^7 lb. per sq. in.?

(3) A metal rod 0·75 in. diameter is tested in a tensile testing machine. When the pull on the specimen is 8000 lb. the total extension over a length of 8 in. is shown by 31 divisions on the scale of an extensometer. If each scale division is equivalent to an extension of 1/5000 in. determine (a) the stress in the bar, (b) the strain and (c) the modulus of elasticity for the material.

(4) The total load on the cylinder cover of a steam engine due to steam pressure is 5 tons. Determine the stress in the bolts required to hold the cover down given that there are 5 bolts each 0·75 in. diameter.

(5) A rod 100 in. long and of diameter 0·5 in. hangs vertically and is loaded at its lower end. Various loads are applied to the lower end and the corresponding extension is given by the following results:

Load lb. ..	100	200	300	400	500	600
Extension in.	0·0043	0·0085	0·013	0·017	0·022	0·026

Plot the graph of load against extension and determine the tensile stress under the maximum load.

(6) Determine the load in lb. which will produce a stress of 10 tons per sq. in. in a wire of diameter 0·1 in. What will be the extension in the wire if its length is 20 ft. and the modulus of elasticity is 12,500 tons per sq. in.?

(7) A round brass rod in tension carries a load of 5 tons. Calculate the diameter of the rod if the stress is not to exceed 3 tons per sq. in. What will the total extension be if the rod is 6 ft. long and the modulus of elasticity is 4,500 tons per sq. in. ?

(8) A circular section bar is made up of two diameters, 3 in. and 2 in. It is subjected to an axial pull of 3 tons. Determine the stress in each portion of the bar and the extension produced in a length of 5 in. in the 3 in. diameter portion. Modulus of elasticity is 12,500 tons per sq. in.

(9) A 4 in. diameter bar is turned down for a part of its length to a diameter of 3·5 in. Determine the maximum tensile load which can be applied to the bar along its axis in order that the stress in the 3·5 in. diameter portion shall not exceed 6 tons per sq. in. What will then be the stress in the 4 in. diameter portion ?

(10) A steel rod 0·75 in. diameter carries a pull of 6 tons. Calculate the extension in inches on a length of 1 ft.

$$(E = 29,000,000 \text{ lb. per sq. in.)} \qquad \text{N.C.T.E.C.}$$

(11) The wire rope of a crane has a cross sectional area of $1\frac{1}{4}$ sq. in. and a modulus of elasticity of 10,000 tons per sq. in. Calculate the stretch of the rope when the length is 40 ft. and the load is 5 tons.

N.C.T.E.C.

(12) State and explain Hooke's Law.

In a tensile test on a steel wire 30 ft. long and 0·02 in. diameter it is found that the modulus of elasticity is 12,500 tons per sq. in. Calculate the load and extension when the stress is 15 tons per sq. in. What would have been the corresponding values for a wire of 0·04 in. diameter ?   N.C.T.E.C.

(13) State Hooke's Law.

A mild steel bar 10 in. long has a diameter of $\frac{3}{4}$ in. for 6 in. of its length and is $1\frac{1}{4}$ in. diameter for the remainder. It is subjected to a direct pull of 2 tons. Given that E for steel is 30×10^6 lb. per sq. in., determine (a) the stress in each part of the bar in lb. per sq. in., (b) the total extension in the bar.   N.C.T.E.C.

(14) A mild steel test piece 0·564 in. diameter and 4 in. gauge length, was subjected to a tensile test until it broke. The extension at various loads was noted and a load-extension graph was drawn. Sketch the general shape you would expect this graph to take.

At a point within the elastic limit the extension was found to be 0·0025 in. and the load 2·03 tons, these values being read from the graph. Determine the value of the modulus of elasticity of the steel.

N.C.T.E.C.

(15) Define " stress," " strain," and " modulus of elasticity."

In an experiment on a wire, 0·06 in. diameter and 9 ft. long a load of 40 lb. produced an extension of 0·052 in. Calculate the stress and strain.   N.C.T.E.C.

(16) A metal bar of length 10 in. and cross sectional area 0·25 sq. in. is gradually loaded in tension up to the elastic limit. From the load extension graph it is found that a load of 2½ tons produces an extension of 0·0084 in. Find Young's Modulus for the metal.   N.C.T.E.C.

(17) The following corresponding set of readings were taken during the test of a helical spring.

Load in lb.   ..   4   8   12   16   20

Length of spring
in inches   ..   4⅛   4½   4⅞   5¼   5⅝

Draw a graph showing the relationship between the load (horizontal) and the spring length (vertical). From the graph find the length of the unloaded spring, and the length when carrying a load of 14 lb.

U.E.I.

(18) Define " Young's Modulus " and " factor of safety."
A tie rod is 30 ft. long. Calculate the change in length when it is subjected to a working stress of 5 tons per sq. in.

(Young's Modulus = 30,000,000 lb. per sq. in.)

U.E.I.

(19) Sketch a typical load-extension curve, marking clearly the following points : (a) limit of proportionality, (b) the yield point, (c) the maximum load.

Calculate the diameter of a steel tie rod which is required to transmit a pull of 6 tons if the ultimate tensile stress of the steel is 30 tons per sq. in., and the factor of safety is to be 6.   U.L.C.I.

(20) What do you understand by the terms " strain," " stress," and " modulus of elasticity " ? A tie rod 100 ft. long and 2 sq. in. cross sectional area is stretched by ¾ in. under a tension of 32,000 lb. What is the intensity of the stress, the strain, and the modulus of elasticity ?

U.L.C.I.

(21) State Hooke's Law. What do you understand by the limit of proportionality of a material ?

An iron bar is 40 ft. long, its section being 3 sq. in. Calculate the maximum load in lb. it can carry if its extension is not to exceed 1/16th in.

(Modulus of elasticity = 29,000,000 lb. per sq. in.)

U.L.C.I.

CHAPTER 5

WORK, ENERGY, AND POWER

Work

When a 7 lb. weight is lifted from the floor to a table 4 ft. high, we say that work is done. If a force of 3 lb. is required to slide a block over a surface for a distance of 10 ft., again we say that work is done.

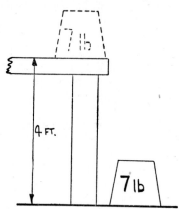

FIG. 39—WORK

To lift the weight with a uniform speed a force of 7 lb. has to be applied. If the weight has to be lifted 4 ft. the force must act through a distance of 4 ft. The work which is done in lifting the weight is given by the product of force and distance. In this case the work done is 28 ft. lb.

The doing of mechanical work always involves two factors :
    (1) *Force.*
    (2) *Movement or displacement.*

Unless both these factors are present, no work is done. The two main forces with which we shall have to deal are :

(1) Force to overcome gravity, i.e., in problems involving lifting.

(2) Force to overcome friction.

Definition.—**Work is said to be done when a force, overcoming a resistance, moves through a distance.**

The unit of work is the " foot-pound " (ft. lb.) and is the amount of work done when a force overcomes a resistance of 1 lb. while moving through a distance of 1 ft. So that in the examples quoted above the amount of work which is done in lifting the 7 lb. weight is $7 \times 4 = 28$ ft. lb. Or in the second example the work done is $3 \times 10 = 30$ ft. lb. in sliding the block on the ground.

$$\text{Work (ft. lb.)} = \text{force (lb.)} \times \text{distance (ft.)}$$

Notice that all this is independent of time. The same amount of work is done in lifting the weight whether we take 2 sec. or 3 min. to do the lifting.

Example 24.—In climbing a slight incline, 200 yds. long, an engine exerts a force of 250 lb. on the trailer. Calculate the total work done by the engine.

Work done = force × distance
= 250 × (200 × 3) (distance in ft.)
= 150,000 ft. lb.   **Ans.**

Example 25.—How much work is done in pumping 500 galls. of water from a well 20 ft. deep? If the water is lifted in 5 min. what is the average work done per min.?

1 gall. of water weighs 10 lb.

∴ weight of water to be lifted   = 500 × 10 lb.
= 5000 lb.
Force required to lift this   = 5000 lb.
Work done   = force × distance
= 5000 × 20
= 100,000 ft. lb.   **Ans.**

Average work done per min. $= \dfrac{100,000}{5}$

= 20,000 ft. lb. per min.   **Ans.**

Example 26.—The diameter of a steam engine piston is 12 in. and the stroke is 10 in. long. During the stroke the average pressure inside the cylinder is 100 lb. per sq. in. The engine makes 40 strokes per min.

How much work is done (*a*) per stroke,
(*b*) per minute?

Area of piston $= \dfrac{\pi}{4} \times 12^2 = 36\pi$ sq. in.

Average force on piston = pressure × area
= 100 × 36π
= 3600π lb.

Distance travelled per stroke $= \dfrac{10}{12}$ ft.

Work done per stroke $= 3600\pi \times \dfrac{10}{12}$

= 3000π
= 9424·8 ft. lb.   **Ans.**

Work done per minute = work done per stroke × strokes per min.

= 9424·8 × 40
= 376,992 ft. lb.   **Ans.**

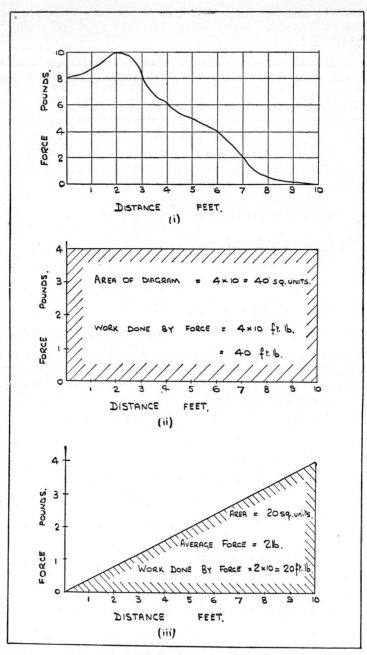

FIG. 40—FORCE–DISTANCE GRAPHS.

Example 27.—A train weighing 300 tons is brought to rest in 200 yds. by a braking force equal to 150 lb. per ton weight of train. There is also a resistance due to friction and air acting parallel to the track of 20 lb. per ton weight. How much work is done in bringing the train to rest?

Total force opposing motion = 150 + 20
= 170 lb. per ton weight of train
= 170 × 300 lb.
= 51,000 lb.

Distance through which this force is acting = 200 × 3
= 600 ft.

Work done in stopping train = 51,000 × 600
= **30,600,000 ft. lb.   Ans.**

Force-Distance Graphs

Although we have only considered work done by a force of constant magnitude, this is by no means the only type of problem involving work done with which we shall have to deal. In the majority of cases the magnitude of the force is not constant, but varies throughout the displacement over which it acts. The variation can be shown graphically as in Fig. 40 (i). Here the force increases from 8 lb. at zero displacement to a maximum of 10 lb. at a distance of 2 ft., and then decreases to zero at a total displacement of 10 ft.

If the force remains constant throughout the movement then the force-distance graph will be as shown in Fig. 40 (ii). The 4 lb. force acts throughout the 10 ft. displacement and therefore 4 × 10 = 40 ft. lb. of work is done. Notice that the shaded area of the diagram is given by 4 × 10 = 40 square units. *Thus the area under the force-distance graph is numerically equal to the work done by the force.* This is true for all types of force variation. In Fig. 40 (iii) the force is represented as increasing uniformly from 0 to 4 lb. during the 10 ft. displacement. The average force acting is therefore 2 lb., and the work done by this force is 2 × 10 = 20 ft. lb. The area of the force-distance triangle is:
$\frac{1}{2}$ base × height
= $\frac{1}{2}$ 10 × 4
= 20 square units.

In the same way we can determine the work done by the force graphically represented in Fig. 40 (i) by using one of the methods for obtaining the area under the curve.

Methods of Determining Area under Curve

1. *Counting Squares.* Count the number of whole squares. If the curve passes through a square, count the square in the total provided that more than half the area of the square is under the curve. If less than half the area is under the curve then neglect the square.

By this method the area under the curve in Fig. 40 (i) is 26 square units representing 52 ft. lb. of work. Each square represents 2 × 1 = 2 ft. lb. of work.

2. *Mid Ordinate Method.* Divide the total base into a suitable number of equal parts and erect ordinates at the mid point of the base of each strip. Each strip is then considered to have an area equal to the base × mid ordinate length. Since each strip has the same width of base, the total area is equal to the sum of the mid ordinates multiplied by the width of one strip.

By this method the area under the curve in Fig. 40 (i) is given by 1 (8·3 + 9·3 + 9·7 + 6·8 + 5·5 + 4·6 + 3·0 + 1·0 + 0·3 + 0·1) = 48·6 square units representing 48·6 ft. lb. of work.

3. *Simpson's Rule.* The most accurate method of the three.

Divide the base into an even number of equal parts and erect ordinates at each point of division. Number the first ordinate 1, the next 2, and so on, finishing with an odd number. The area of the figure is given by

$$\text{Area} = \frac{\text{width of one strip}}{3} \times \text{sum of} \begin{bmatrix} \text{first} + \text{last ordinate} \\ 2 \times \text{sum of odd ordinates} \\ 4 \times \text{sum of even ordinates.} \end{bmatrix}$$

The first and the last ordinates must not be included in the sum of the odd ordinates.

Applying this rule to Fig. 40 (i) we have:

First and last	odd	even
8·0	10·0	8·7
0	6·0	8·0
———	4·0	5·0
8·0	0·5	2·0
———	———	0·2
	20·5	———
	2	23·9
	———	4
	41·0	———
	———	95·6

$$\text{Area} = \frac{1}{3} \times \begin{bmatrix} 8 \cdot 0 + 41 \cdot 0 + 95 \cdot 6 \end{bmatrix}$$

= 48·2 square units representing 48·2 ft. lb. of work.

Example 28.—In an experiment with a truck which was pulled over a horizontal table the tractive force F was measured by a spring balance at various distances x from the start. The readings were as follows:

F lb.	70	58	50	34	20	10
x ft.	0	6	10	18	25	30

Plot the curve showing the relationship between the tractive force and the distance x. Determine the work done in pulling the truck over the 30 ft.

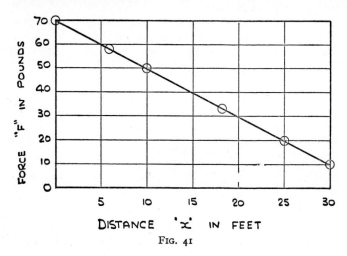

FORCE "F" IN POUNDS

DISTANCE 'x' IN FEET

FIG. 41

The graph showing variation of force with distance is a straight line. (Fig. 41.)

The work done in pulling truck is represented by the area under the graph.

i.e., by the area of the trapezium = ½ sum of parallel sides × distance between them.

Work done = ½ [70 + 10] × 30
        =1200 ft. lb.   Ans.

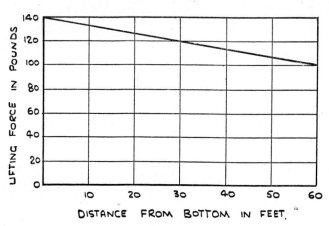

LIFTING FORCE IN POUNDS

DISTANCE FROM BOTTOM IN FEET.

FIG. 42

Example 29.—A cage weighs 100 lb. and the haulage rope weighs two-thirds of a pound per foot length. If the cage is at the bottom of a shaft 60 ft. deep, determine the work done in raising it to the top of the shaft.

The force required to lift the cage and rope will gradually decrease as more rope is wound on to the drum.

When the cage is at the bottom of the shaft, force required to lift = weight of cage + weight of rope

$$= 100 + (60 \times \tfrac{2}{3})$$
$$= 140 \text{ lb.}$$

When the cage is at the top of the shaft the force is reduced to 100 lb., i.e., the weight of the cage. The force-distance graph is shown in Fig. 42.

Work done = area under graph

$$= \tfrac{1}{2}(140 + 100) \times 60$$
$$= 120 \times 60$$
$$= \textbf{7200 ft. lb. \quad Ans.}$$

Example 30.—A spring balance was inserted between a motor and a truck in order to measure the pull exerted by the motor. The readings P lb. of the balance were taken at distances S yds. from the starting point and were as follows:

P lb. ..	180	130	104	88	86	96	108	195·5	125	125	115
S yds. ..	0	100	200	300	350	400	450	500	550	600	700

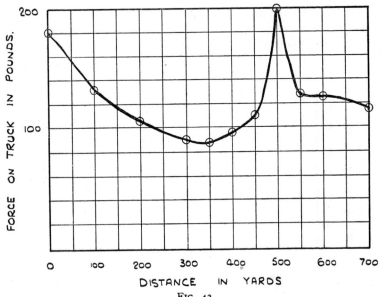

FORCE ON TRUCK IN POUNDS.

DISTANCE IN YARDS

Fig. 43

Plot a curve connecting P and S, plotting P vertically and using this curve find the average pull exerted. What is the work done in ft. tons in hauling the truck over the 700 yds.?   U.E.I.

The curve is shown in Fig. 43.

The work done in hauling the truck is represented by the area under the graph.

Area (by counting squares) = 83 units.

This represents $83 \times 20 \times 50 \times 3$

$\qquad\qquad = 249{,}000$ ft. lb. work.

1 vertical unit equals 20 lb.

1 horizontal unit equals $50 \times 3 = 150$ ft.

$$\therefore \text{ work done} = \frac{249{,}000}{2240} \text{ ft. tons}$$

$$= 111 \text{ ft. tons.} \quad \textbf{Ans.}$$

$$\text{Average pull} = \frac{\text{work done}}{\text{distance moved}}$$

$$= \frac{249{,}000}{700 \times 3} \text{ using ft. lb. and ft. units.}$$

$$= 118 \cdot 5 \text{ lb.} \quad \textbf{Ans.}$$

This means that a constant force of $118\frac{1}{2}$ lb. would do the same amount of work in moving the 700 yds. as the varying force does.

Using Simpson's Rule for area we have :

First and last	2 × odd	4 × even
180	130	155
115	104	116
———	88	96
295	96	86
———	195·5	108
	125	125
	———	122
	738·5	———
	2	808
	———	4
	1477	———
	———	3232

$$\text{Area} = \frac{50}{3} [295 + 1477 + 3232]$$

$$= \frac{50}{3} \times 5004$$

$$= \frac{250{,}200}{3} \text{ in lb. and yd. units}$$

$$= 250{,}200 \text{ in lb. and ft. units.}$$

$$\therefore \text{ work done} = 250{,}200 \text{ ft. lb.} \quad \textbf{Ans.}$$

This gives an average force of 119·2 lb.

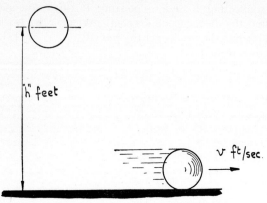

h" feet

v ft/sec

FIG. 44—MECHANICAL ENERGY
The two spheres possess different forms of Mechanical Energy. That on the left has Potential Energy or energy due to its position. The work which was done in lifting the sphere to a height h ft. is stored in the body. The sphere is capable of doing work when it is dropped. The sphere on the right possesses Kinetic Energy or energy due to its velocity. In order to move the body with a velocity of v ft. per sec. work had to be done on the body. This work is stored in the sphere as Kinetic Energy. If the body is brought to rest it will give up that energy in doing work.

Energy

By energy we mean the capacity to do work.

A heavy block can be lifted to a height by doing work on the block. This work is stored in the block. If the block is now released and allowed to fall on to a slab of stone, it may break the stone. The work required to break the stone is equal to the work stored in the block. We say that the block possesses energy when it is suspended because it is capable of doing work when it is released. *The energy which it possesses is equal to the amount of work which was done in lifting it.*

A compressed spring possesses energy. When the spring is released it can be made to do work. *The amount of work which it can do is equal to the work done in compressing the spring.*

The unit of energy is the foot-pound, the same unit which we use for work.

There are many kinds of energy, of which the following are the ones with which we shall have to be familiar.

1. *Mechanical Energy.*

    (*a*) Potential, i.e., energy due to position.

            Examples: The block and spring just considered. Water at a high level such as at a waterfall or in a stream at the top of a mountain.

    (*b*) Kinetic, i.e., energy due to motion.

            Example: Jet of water directed against a moving blade in water turbine.

2. *Heat Energy.*   Example: Heat stored in steam for use in steam engine or turbine.

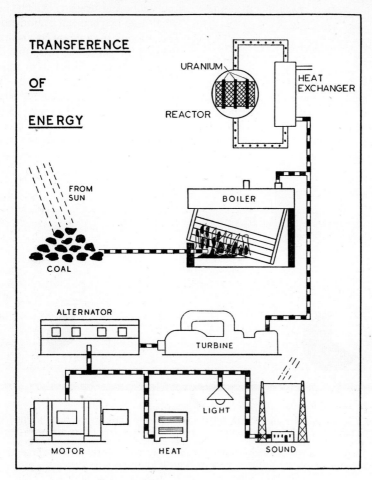

TRANSFERENCE

OF

ENERGY

URANIUM

HEAT
EXCHANGER

REACTOR

FROM
SUN

COAL

BOILER

ALTERNATOR

TURBINE

LIGHT

MOTOR   HEAT   SOUND

FIG. 45—TRANSFERENCE OF ENERGY

Chemical Energy, received from the sun and stored in coal, can be released by combustion and converted into Heat and Pressure Energy by a boiler. Alternatively Atomic Energy stored in uranium can be released by fission in a reactor and converted into Heat and Pressure Energy in a heat exchanger. From either source the Heat and Pressure Energy is conveyed in steam to a heat engine which converts the energy into Mechanical (Kinetic) Energy. This energy is used to drive an alternator which converts the Mechanical Energy into Electrical Energy. A radiator will convert the Electrical Energy into Heat Energy and to a certain extent into Light Energy. This last change is more noticeable with an electric light bulb. Conversion can also be made into sound by suitable equipment. If the Electrical Energy is supplied to an electric motor it is converted back again into Mechanical (Kinetic) Energy and could be used to obtain a further supply of coal or uranium and so repeat the cycle.

3. *Chemical Energy.* Example : Coal contains energy which can be released by chemical combustion. The energy in gunpowder is also released in the same way but in a much shorter interval of time.

4. *Electrical Energy.*

There is a very fundamental principle dealing with questions of energy which is known as the Principle of the Conservation of Energy. *This states that energy can neither be created nor destroyed.* It can be transferred from one form to another. An example of this transference is shown in Fig. 45.

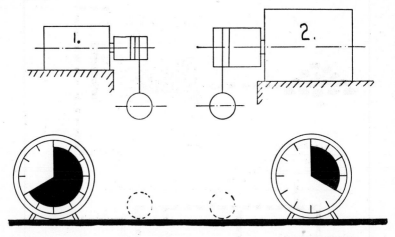

FIG. 46—POWER

Two machines 1 and 2 both lift the same weight through the same height. They both do the same amount of work. Machine No. 1 does the work in twice the time taken by machine No. 2. No. 2 is therefore twice as powerful as No. 1. Power takes time into account. It is a measure of how much work is done in unit time.

Power

We have already seen that the amount of work required to lift a load of 500 lb. through a distance of 10 ft. is equal to 5000 ft. lb. and does not depend upon the time taken in the lifting process. Suppose that we have two machines A and B. We can lift the load in 2 minutes if we use machine A, while B takes 5 minutes to lift it. Both machines do the same amount of work, but A is working at the **RATE** of 2500 ft. lb. per min. while B is working at the **RATE** of 1000 ft. lb. per min. We say that A is the more powerful machine of the two. *When we discuss power we shall always be thinking of the rate at which the work is done.* In other words we shall be thinking of " foot-pounds per minute " or "foot-pounds per second."

Definition.—**Power is the rate of doing work.**

In the days in which James Watt and his friends were developing the steam engine, horses were being used in large numbers to drive various machines in the country. They were used particularly in the pumping operations which had to be done in connection with the mines in Cornwall and the north-eastern counties. It was the intention of Watt to replace these horses with his engines and therefore as a basis of comparison, so that he could state how many horses could be replaced by his engines, he decided to find out the *rate at which an average horse worked*. In other words, how many foot-pounds of work the average horse could do

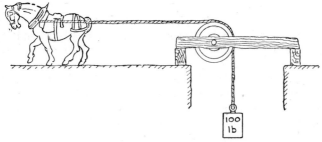

FIG. 47—JAMES WATT'S EXPERIMENT TO DETERMINE THE POWER OF
A HORSE.

When Watt wanted to replace existing horse-driven machines with his new engines he had to answer the question: " How many horses will your machine replace ?" So he set out to determine how much work an average horse could do in one minute. In the year 1784 he carried out his experiment with a brewer's dray horse. The horse had to pull a weight of 100 lb. out of a deep shaft by means of a rope passing over a pulley. Watt calculated the steady speed of the horse during the operation. This was found to be 2½ miles per hour. By making certain corrections " to be on the safe side " Watt established that a horse would work at a rate of 33,000 ft. lb. per minute. This unit of power is the horsepower.

in one minute. In the test which he carried out, he allowed a strong dray horse to lift a load of 100 lb. vertically up a mine shaft by means of a pulley and rope. The average speed with which the horse could lift the 100 lb. load was approximately 2½ m.p.h. or 220 ft. per min. So the horse was doing 220 × 100 = 22,000 ft. lb. of work per min. Watt increased this figure by 50% so that he would be on the safe side in calculations relating to his engines. He therefore used the figure of 33,000 ft. lb. per min. as the basis of his calculations. This figure has been accepted as the standard unit of power and is called the horse-power.

> **One horsepower = 33,000 ft. lb. per min.**
> **One horsepower = 550 ft. lb. per sec.**

An engine is said to develop 1 *horsepower* (h.p.) *if it can do work at the rate of* 33,000 *ft. lb. per min.*

$$\text{Horsepower} = \frac{\text{work done per min.}}{33,000}$$

$$\text{Horsepower} = \frac{\text{work done per sec.}}{550}$$

Electrical Unit of Power

The unit of power used in electrical work is **the watt**. The kilowatt is equal to 1000 watts.

$$\text{1 horsepower} = 746 \text{ watts} = 0\cdot746 \text{ kilowatt.}$$

If an electrical machine is working at the rate of 1 kilowatt for 1 hour the amount of electrical energy used is **1 kilowatt-hour**, usually referred to as **one unit**.

A 2-kilowatt fire burning for 3 hours consumes 6 kilowatt-hours or 6 units of electrical energy. If the cost of this energy is ¼d. per unit then the cost of operating a 2-kilowatt fire for 3 hours will be threepence.

Example 31.—In climbing a slight incline 200 yds. long an engine exerts a force of 250 lb. on the trailer. If the speed of the engine is 20 m.p.h., calculate the average horsepower exerted during the climb.

$$20 \text{ m.p.h.} = 20 \times 5280 \text{ ft. per hour}$$
$$= \frac{20 \times 5280}{60} \text{ ft. per min.}$$
$$= 1760 \text{ ft. per min.}$$

Force exerted by engine $= 250$ lb.

Work done by engine per min. $=$ force $\times$ distance moved per min.
$$= 250 \times 1760 \text{ ft. lb. per min.}$$

$$\therefore \text{ horsepower exerted} = \frac{250 \times 1760}{33,000}$$
$$= 13\cdot33 \text{ h.p.} \quad \textbf{Ans.}$$

Example 32.—A motor-car is travelling at 45 m.p.h. along a straight level road. If the weight of the car is 25 cwt. and the road and wind resistances amount to 40 lb. per ton, what horsepower is being absorbed in propelling the car? If the car now reaches a slope of 1 vertical in 100 along the slope, what additional horsepower will be required to maintain the speed of 45 m.p.h.?

N.C.T.E.C.

$$45 \text{ m.p.h.} = 45 \times 5280 \text{ ft. per hour}$$
$$= \frac{45 \times 5280}{60} \text{ ft. per min.}$$
$$= 3960 \text{ ft. per min.}$$

Total resistance $=$ resistance per ton $\times$ weight of car in tons

$$= 40 \times \frac{25}{20} \text{ lb.}$$

$$= 50 \text{ lb.}$$

Work done per min. = force × distance moved per min.

$$= 50 \times 3960 \text{ ft. lb. per min.}$$

∴ horsepower absorbed $= \dfrac{50 \times 3960}{33,000}$

$$= 6 \text{ h.p. } \textbf{Ans.}$$

When the car begins to climb the hill it has to overcome the gravitational effect, trying to pull it back down the hill.

Force pulling car back downhill $= 25 \times \dfrac{1}{100}$ cwt.   (see Example 9)

$$= \frac{25 \times 112}{100}$$

$$= 28 \text{ lb.}$$

A driving force of 28 lb. has to be produced to overcome this tendency to pull back, in addition to the 50 lb. force which must still act to overcome wind and friction resistances.

Additional work done per min. in climbing at 45 m.p.h.

$$= \text{force} \times \text{distance moved per min.}$$

$$= 28 \times 3960$$

Additional h.p. $= \dfrac{28 \times 3960}{33,000}$

$$= 3 \cdot 36 \text{ h.p.}$$

∴ total h.p. required to climb hill at 45 m.p.h. overcoming wind and friction resistance $= 3 \cdot 36 + 6$

$$= 9 \cdot 36 \text{ h.p. } \textbf{Ans.}$$

EXERCISE 4

(1) A vehicle weighing 6 tons is travelling at 20 m.p.h. against resistances of 20 lb. per ton. What horsepower is required to drive the vehicle :

    (a) on the level,

    (b) up an incline of 1 in 12 ?

(2) Find the speed in m.p.h. at which a locomotive engine weighing 24 tons and developing 160 h.p. can draw a train of weight 120 tons along a horizontal track if the resistance to motion is 10 lb. per ton weight.

(3) An omnibus weighs 8 tons. The frictional resistance to motion of the omnibus is 20 lb. for each ton of its weight.

Calculate the work done by a crane in lifting it through a vertical distance of 8 ft.

M.E.S.I—3

Calculate also the work done by the omnibus if it is driven through a distance of 8 ft. along a horizontal road.

(4) A locomotive draws a train of total weight 500 tons along a level track at a speed of 40 m.p.h. If the tractive resistance is constant and equal to 12 lb. per ton, at what horsepower must the engine be working?

(5) A tank at ground level contains 1000 gallons of water which are to be pumped to the roof of a building 80 ft. high in 12 min. What must be the horsepower of the motor driving the pump:

    (a) assuming no losses,

    (b) assuming that the pump loses 30% of the power supplied, in friction, etc.?

    1 gall. of water weighs 10 lb.

(6) A chain 200 ft. long hangs from a drum. At the end of the chain is a load of 50 lb. If the chain weighs 2 lb. per ft. of length determine the work done in lifting up this load 40 ft. by winding in the chain. Draw a diagram representing work done.

(7) A horizontal force of 60 lb. is required to keep a block of stone weighing 200 lb. moving with steady motion along a horizontal surface. The block is moved through a distance of 1500 ft. in 10 min. What horsepower is expended in moving the block?

(8) A canal lock 150 ft. long and 9 ft. wide contains water to a height of 10 ft. above the level of the canal. If the lock is to be filled to this height in 20 min. what is the horsepower of the pump? Assume no losses. Density of water 64 lb. per cubic ft.

(9) A body has a variable pull P lb. acting on it. Values of P and the distance D from rest are as follows:

D ft.	..	0	2	5	8	10·5	14	18	22	25	30
P lb.	..	15	20	25	25	24	20	12	8	4	0

Plot a curve showing the variation of pull and distance. What is the average pull? What is the total work done?

(10) Define " work " and " power." In climbing a slight incline, 300 yds. long, the average force exerted by an engine on a trailer is 240 lb. Calculate the total work done. If the speed is 15 m.p.h., calculate the average horsepower exerted during the climb.   U.E.I.

(11) Define " work " and " horsepower."

A train weighing 250 tons experiences a frictional resistance of 15 lb. per ton. Find (a) the work done in pulling the train 100 yds. along a level track, and (b) the horsepower exerted in pulling the train at 45 m.p.h. up an incline of 1 in 200.   U.E.I.

(12) A passenger lift of total weight 35 cwt. travels vertically upwards at a uniform speed of 2 ft. per sec. with an efficiency of 60%. Calculate:

    (a) the work done if the lift travels 90 ft.,

    (b) the horsepower required to drive the lift.   U.E.I.

(13) A traction engine working against a total resistance of 480 lb. does 330,000 ft. lb. of work per min. How far does it travel in one minute and what is its speed in m.p.h. ? U.E.I.

(14) Explain what is meant by " a foot-pound of work."
A man performed 21 in. tons of work in raising a lorry by means of a jack. How many foot-pounds of work were done ? If the man applied a force of 32 lb. throughout each working stroke of length 15 in. assuming no lost work, how many working strokes did he make ? U.E.I.

(15) A machine casting weighs 480 lb. How many foot-pounds of work would be expended :
    (a) in raising it vertically through a height of 66 in.,
    (b) in moving it 5 ft. over a horizontal bed plate, the resisting force being 0·24 lb. per pound weight of the casting. U.E.I.

(16) A cyclist, moving against an average total resistance of 15 lb., travels a distance of 10 miles in one hour. Calculate the amount of work done in one minute in foot-pounds. U.E.I.

(17) A body is being acted upon by a variable lifting force. When the body is lifted S ft., the force P lb. is observed :

S ..	0	10	20	30	40	50	60	70
P ..	850	810	720	605	495	390	300	250

Find the average lifting force and the work done by P in lifting the body 70 ft. U.E.I.

(18) Distinguish between " work " and " power."
A load of 5 tons is raised a vertical distance of 20 yds. in $\frac{3}{4}$ min. by an electric crane. Assuming an ideal machine, calculate (a) the average power of the motor, and (b) the cost of electrical energy if the charge is 0·5d. per kilowatt-hour. One horsepower = 746 watts. N.C.T.E.C.

(19) Water is raised 100 ft. by a pump driven by a 40 h.p. motor. If 50 per cent. of the energy supplied by the motor is employed in useful work calculate the rate of pumping in cubic ft. per hour. Density of water = 62·5 lb. per cubic ft. N.C.T.E.C.

(20) Give the physical dimensions of " power " in terms of force, length, and time.
A boy is employed lifting articles weighing 14 oz. from the ground to a height of 4 ft. 9 in. If he lifts 80 articles in 4 min. find the average horsepower. N.C.T.E.C.

(21) A lift cage weighing 30 cwt. is raised steadily through a height of 30 ft. The ropes weigh $\frac{1}{2}$ lb. per foot length and there are 2 such ropes used. Draw a diagram to scale representing the total work done in lifting and determine the numerical value of that work.
If the lift is accomplished in 9 sec., what is the horsepower expended in lifting ? Neglect friction losses. N.C.T.E.C.

(22) A small loaded truck, total weight of 3 tons, is pulled up a slope of 1 in 6 (measured along the slope) by means of a wire rope from a winch

at the top of the slope. Neglecting friction, determine the pull in the rope when the truck is moving up the slope at uniform speed. Find also the thrust on the truck under those conditions.   If the truck has a uniform speed of 300 ft. per min. up the incline, determine the horsepower exerted by the winch.   N.C.T.E.C.

(23) Explain the difference between " work " and " power."

A crane is driven by an electric motor of 10 h.p. If 40 per cent. of the energy supplied does useful work, calculate the least time required to raise a load of 3 tons vertically through 40 ft. assuming a constant speed of lift.   N.C.T.E.C.

(24) Define " work " and " power."

A colliery engine hauls a load of 20 tons vertically up a shaft 2000 ft. deep in $1\frac{1}{2}$ min. Calculate the work done and the average useful horsepower exerted by the engine.   N.C.T.E.C.

(25) Show how work can be represented graphically.

A load of 15 tons is raised through a height of 20 ft. If the average useful horsepower is 5, find the time taken to raise the load.

N.C.T.E.C.

(26) Explain the statement " the power of a machine is one horsepower." A weight of 1 ton is raised 15 ft. by a crane. What work is done ?   If the lifting takes half a minute, what is the effective horsepower of the crane motor ?   U.L.C.I.

(27) The cutting stroke of a planing machine, which cuts in both directions, is 8 ft. The number of single strokes made per hour is 170 and the average resistance to cutting is 420 lb.   Find the horsepower absorbed in cutting.   U.L.C.I.

(28) The following table gives the forces F lb. acting on a moving body at different distances x ft. from an initial position :

| F lb. .. | 10 | 17 | 25 | 38 | 45 | 50 |
| x ft. .. | 0 | 7 | 15 | 28 | 35 | 40 |

Draw to scale the diagram of work and find the number of foot-pounds of work the diagram represents.   U.L.C.I.

CHAPTER 6

FRICTION

It is a strange state of affairs in the engineering world that whilst one team of designers are using all efforts to make wheels turn more efficiently, another team of designers are expending equal efforts to prevent wheels from turning. One company are working to produce bigger and better accelerations while another company works to produce bigger and better retardations. The second company have a great advantage over the first. There is an ever present natural force which tends to slow down and ultimately stop any moving object. It is not natural for bodies to increase in speed, their natural tendency is to slow down. *This " slowing down " force is due to friction.* It is friction forces, acting in the bearings, which cause rotating wheels to slow down and come to rest after the driving force has been shut off. It is friction forces, together with wind resistances, which will bring to rest a trolley moving over a horizontal rail.

Therefore if we want to keep either the wheel rotating or the trolley moving at constant speed we shall have to supply a driving force for no other reason than to overcome friction forces. When a car is moving over a horizontal road at constant speed we only require a tractive effort sufficient to overcome friction in bearings and resistance due to wind. This force will generally be considerably smaller than that required to start the car from rest, or to increase the speed of the car once it has begun to move, or to drive it up a hill. In fact if we could eliminate the friction forces and cut out the wind resistances then the car would keep going at any constant speed without any tractive effort, and that means in other words without any petrol. Once the car has reached any desired speed it will maintain this speed until it either comes into contact with another object, or we introduce friction in large quantities by applying the brakes. The nearest that we can approach to this condition of perfection (without going into the stratosphere) is to think of a steel ball bearing moving over a level sheet of ice. You will need to apply a force to start the ball moving, but once it is moving it will continue in the direction until it meets some obstacle such as the edge of the pond or some irregularity on the surface of the ice. The frictional resisting forces acting between the ball and the surface over which it is moving have been practically eliminated. That is the reason why a sledge will move much farther over

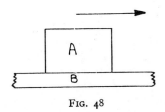

Fig. 48

75

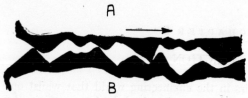

FIG. 49—A considerably enlarged diagram showing two " smooth " surfaces in contact. The force required to move A over B due to the irregularities of the surface is called the friction force.

ice or snow than it will over a normal road surface, assuming that the same initial starting force is applied in each case. Consider now two bodies A and B in contact (Fig. 48). Although the two surfaces in contact appear to be very smooth, we shall find if we examine the surfaces under a profile recording machine that they are actually as shown in Fig. 49. You will therefore realise why a force is required to move A over B. The effect of pouring a lubricant between the surfaces is to lift A off B as shown in Fig. 50. In effect A floats on the surface of an oil film. Thus we can reduce friction forces by supplying a lubricant, and we can increase friction forces by increasing the roughness of the contacting surfaces. The engineer finds it necessary to perform both these operations. If a shaft is to run freely in its bearings he

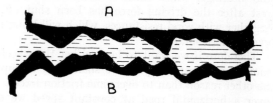

FIG. 50—The two surfaces have now been lubricated. A suitable oil is introduced between the surfaces and A now " floats " on the oil film.

supplies plenty of lubricant, or alternatively he mounts the shaft in ball or roller bearings so that the surfaces which are in contact and have relative motion are as smooth and as hard as modern engineering practice will allow. If, on the other hand, he wants to bring the rotating shaft to rest he can bring into contact with the moving surface of the wheel a rough material, such as leather or " Ferodo," as is used in brake design.

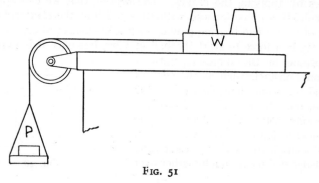

FIG. 51

A force of P lb. is applied to a block whose total weight is W lb. (Fig. 51). The block is free to move over the horizontal surface. If the force P is insufficient to move the block, *there must be a force equal in magnitude to P but acting in the opposite direction to maintain the equilibrium.* This force is the friction force F. It is always equal and opposite to P provided the block does not move. If P is increased, F will also increase until it reaches a maximum value whose magnitude depends upon:

(i) the nature of the surfaces in contact, including both materials, condition of surface finish and state of lubrication, and
(ii) the weight of the block.

The maximum value of F is called the limiting force of friction. When P is greater than this limiting force the block will move in the direction of P.

Let P lb. = the force required just to move the block with uniform motion
W lb. = the total weight of the moving block.

It is found experimentally that:

$$\frac{P}{W} = \mu$$

and P = μW

where μ (pronounced mu) is a constant called the **coefficient of friction**. Its value depends upon the nature of the surfaces in contact. It is important to notice that its value cannot be greater than 1. The following table gives the value of μ for a number of pairs of surfaces.

TABLE 2

Materials	Coefficient of friction
Bronze on bronze dry	0·2
Bronze on bronze lubricated ..	0·05
Leather on steel	0·55
Wood on steel	0·5
Steel on steel lubricated.. ..	0·1

Example 33.—Calculate the work done in dragging a casting of weight 8 tons a distance of 120 ft. over a rough horizontal surface if the coefficient of friction is 0·75. If the operation takes 10 min., calculate the average horsepower expended.

Horizontal force required $= \mu W$
                                   $= 0.75 \times 8$
                                   $= 6$ tons.
Work done $=$ force $\times$ distance $= 6 \times 120$
                                   $= 720$ ft. tons.   Ans.
Work done per min. $= \dfrac{720}{10}$
                                   $= 72$ ft. tons
                                   $= 72 \times 2240$ ft. lb.
Average horsepower expended $= \dfrac{72 \times 2240}{33,000}$
                                   $= 4.89$ h.p.   Ans.

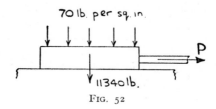

Fig. 52

Example 34.—The sliding face of a steam engine slide valve measures 9 in. × 18 in. and the pressure on the back of the valve is 70 lb. per sq. in. If the coefficient of friction is 0·2 calculate the force required to move the valve.

Area of valve in contact with steam $= 9 \times 18$
                                     $= 162$ sq. in.
Normal force between valve and slide $=$ pressure $\times$ area
  (we are neglecting the weight of the valve)

                                     $= 70 \times 162$
                                     $= 11,340$ lb.
Force required to move valve $= \mu \times$ normal force
                                     $= 0.2 \times 11,340$
                                     $= 2268$ lb.   Ans.

Example 35.—A force of 80 lb., acting as shown in Fig. 53 will just cause a weight W of 200 lb. to slide along a horizontal surface AB.   Determine :

  (a) the work done when the weight moves a distance of 12 ft. in the direction of AB,

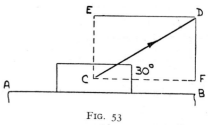

Fig. 53

  (b) the coefficient of friction between the surfaces.

Resolve the force CD into its two components :
   CE vertically,
   CF horizontally.
CF will pull the weight along the surface.
CE will lift the weight upwards. It will therefore reduce the normal force between W and the surface AB.
Vertical component CE = 80 sin 30° (or by measurement)
$$= 40 \text{ lb.}$$
Normal force between W and AB = 200 − 40
$$= 160 \text{ lb.}$$
Horizontal component CF = 80 cos 30° (or by measurement)
$$= 69 \cdot 2 \text{ lb.}$$
∴ work done when weight moves 12 ft. in direction of AB
$$= \text{force in direction of AB} \times 12$$
$$= 69 \cdot 2 \times 12$$
$$= 830 \text{ ft. lb.} \quad \textbf{Ans.}$$

$$\text{Coefficient of friction} = \frac{\text{force to move}}{\text{normal force between surfaces}}$$
$$= \frac{69 \cdot 2}{160}$$
$$= 0 \cdot 43. \quad \textbf{Ans.}$$

EXERCISE 5

(1) A horizontal rope applying a force of 35 lb. to a block of stone weighing 80 lb. pulls it along a level road at uniform speed. If an additional 20 lb. weight is placed on the block what must be the pull in the rope to move the block with uniform speed ? If the rope will not transmit a greater force than 60 lb. what is the greatest weight which can be carried by the block ?

(2) The sliding face of a steam engine slide valve measures 9 in. by $15\frac{1}{2}$ in. and the steam pressure on the back of the valve is 80 lb. per sq. in. If the coefficient of friction is 0·15, calculate the force required to move the valve.

(3) In an experiment to determine the coefficient of friction between steel and brass, a brass slider was placed on a horizontal steel surface. Various weights were placed in succession on the slider, and, for each weight, a horizontal force was applied to the slider so that the slider moved at a uniform slow speed when started by hand. The observations were : Weight of slider, 1 lb.

Additional weight placed on slider (lb.)	2	4	6	8	10	12
Horizontal force required (lb.)	1·2	1·9	2·7	3·5	4·2	5

Determine the average value of the coefficient of friction between the two surfaces.

M.E.S.I—3*

(4) The coefficient of friction between a body weighing 750 lb. and a level surface over which it is being pulled is 0·16.

(a) What horizontal force is required to keep the body moving at a constant speed ?

(b) How much work is done per minute by this force if the body is moving at 4·2 ft. per sec. ?

(c) What horsepower is required to draw the body at the given speed ?

(5) A horizontal force of 60 lb. can keep a block of stone weighing 240 lb. in steady motion along a horizontal surface. What is the coefficient of friction ? If the block is moved through a distance of 1320 ft. in 5 min. what horsepower is expended in overcoming friction ?

(6) A block which weighs $1\frac{1}{2}$ lb. carries a load of W lb. The force P lb. needed to pull it steadily over a rough horizontal surface is given in the table. Determine the average value of the coefficient of friction and estimate the horizontal force required when W = 22 lb.

W lb. ..	4	8	12	16	20	24
P lb. ..	1·5	3·0	4·4	5·4	7·0	8·0

(7) Define " coefficient of friction."

Calculate the work done in ft.-tons in dragging a casting of weight 6 tons over a distance of 100 ft. over a rough horizontal plane if the coefficient of friction is 0·75. If the operation took 5 min. calculate the average horsepower expended.   U.L.C.I.

(8) What do you understand by " coefficient of friction " ?

A body weighing 120 lb. rests on a horizontal table. If the coefficient of friction is 0·2 find the least horizontal force which would move the body. How much work would be done in moving the body over a distance of 1 ft. ?   U.L.C.I.

(9) Friction may be useful or objectionable in a machine. Mention one case of each. Why does lubrication reduce friction ? A block of iron weighing 56 lb. lies on a horizontal table. A flexible string is tied to the block and, after passing horizontally to the edge of the table, passes over a frictionless pulley, and has the other end fastened to a scale pan which weighs $\frac{1}{2}$ lb. If the coefficient of limiting friction between the iron and the table surface is 0·25, what weight must be placed in the pan to cause the iron just to move ?   U.L.C.I.

(10) A force of 150 lb., acting as shown in Fig. 53, will just cause a weight W of 400 lb. to slide along a horizontal surface AB. Determine—

(a) the work done when the weight moves a distance of 12 ft. in the direction AB,

(b) the coefficient of friction.

CHAPTER 7

MACHINES

Very early in his history, man found that he was called upon to carry out tasks which were made difficult, if not impossible, by his own physical weakness. Even the strongest man discovered that there was a limit to the weight which he could lift, and to the load which he could drag over the ground. He therefore tried to devise some means to do the required work without exerting more effort than was necessary. For example, he found that a heavy weight could be lifted easily if a lever was used. He found that a large block of stone could be moved more easily over the ground if a number of rollers were placed under the block and the block pushed over the rollers instead of being dragged over the ground. He found that very heavy stone blocks could be brought more easily into position in such buildings as the Pyramids, if they were brought gradually up a slope or inclined plane. It would have been impossible to lift some of these stones into position since they had no cranes or even " sky-hooks " available. They had, however, a considerable amount of slave labour available, and this labour could be employed in producing a force parallel to the plane in order to pull the blocks into position. In all these instances one fundamental point is to be found. *A large resistance was overcome by means of a relatively small force or effort.* Any arrangement which will produce this result is called a **machine.** The sturdy branches of trees used as levers, the cylindrical tree trunks used as rollers, or the long slope of rubble and brick and stone were just as much machines as the elaborate cranes or the impressive " streamline " engines we see today. In all cases they have been devised so that man can perform his tasks with the exertion of minimum effort on his part. A modern locomotive can draw a train of 300 tons at an average speed of 60 m.p.h. over distances of 400 miles. The performance of the engine is made possible by the physical exertions of the fireman supplying the boiler with coal. These exertions are relatively small compared with the exertions which would have to be made if the train were to be pulled by a team of men. Even if they were capable of travelling at an average speed of 60 m.p.h. (which they are not) a team of at least 1200 men would be required, and they would have to be changed at very frequent intervals.

Now in all machines there are two main parts. The **input side** and the **output side.** The resistance to be overcome or the load is connected to the output side and the effort is applied to the input side. The relationship between the effort and the load depends upon the type of machine which is being used. The relationship gives a good indication of the advantage which can be obtained by using the machine. The relationship is called the **Mechanical Advantage** of the machine.

$$\text{Mechanical advantage} = \frac{\text{load}}{\text{effort.}}$$

If you have seen a casting being lifted into position by means of a pulley block tackle you will have noticed that the casting moves very slowly compared with the rate at which the operator moves the chain on the input side. If you watch the rotation of the shafts of a worm gear box you will see that the output shaft, or the wheel shaft, rotates much more slowly than the input or worm shaft. The ratio between the distances or the angles moved through by the effort at the input side and the load at the output side is the **Velocity Ratio** of the machine.

$$\text{Velocity ratio} = \frac{\text{distance moved by effort}}{\text{distance moved by load in same time.}}$$

When we consider the amount of work which is " put into " the machine by the effort on the input side and also the amount of work which is " got out " of the machine by the load on the output side we shall have to introduce another expression—the **Efficiency** of the machine. As the effort moves through any given distance it does a definite amount of work. During this same interval of time the load is being moved through a certain distance. This is only possible if the machine does the necessary amount of work on the load. The efficiency is the ratio of these two amounts of work. If the machine were perfect, that is, if there were no friction at the bearings, no drag due to windage or the viscous effect of lubricants; if, in the case of a lifting block, the hook and the chain supporting the hook had no weight so that you had only the load to lift and not the parts of the pulley block in addition; if you complied with these conditions then you could expect to get the same amount of work out of the machine as you had put into it.

A diagrammatic

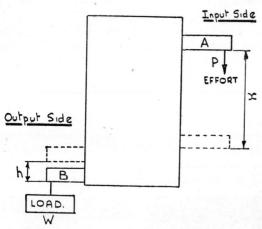

Fig. 54—The Essentials of a Machine

The mechanical advantage is $\dfrac{\text{load}}{\text{effort}} = \dfrac{W}{P}$

Velocity ratio $= \dfrac{\text{distance moved by effort}}{\text{distance moved by load in same time}} = \dfrac{x}{h}$

representation of the essential parts of a machine is shown in Fig. 54. Lever A on the input side is connected to lever B on the output side by means of a system of levers, pulleys, and gears inside the machine. We are not for the moment concerned with the connections between the input and the output sides because these do not affect the basic calculations in connection with the machine. If a weight W lb. is hung on the end of lever B, it is found that an effort of P lb. is required at the end of lever A in order to lift the weight. This means that under these conditions the mechanical advantage of the machine is W/P. That is, you can lift a load of W/P times the effort which you are applying. You will notice however that the load moves much more slowly than the effort. Let the input lever be moved so that the point at which the effort is applied moves through a distance x feet. It will be seen that the point at which the load is applied on the output lever has moved through a distance h feet. This means that the velocity ratio of the machine is equal to x/h; that is, the effort moves x/h times as far as the load moves in the same time.

This is one of the ways in which you can determine the velocity ratio of any machine. Simply measure the distances through which the points of application of the effort and the load move in the same time and calculate the ratio x/h.

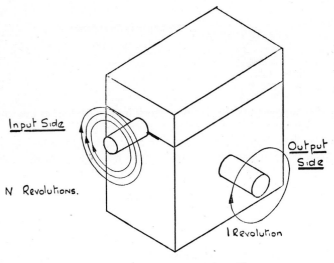

FIG. 55—Velocity ratio = N

If the machine has two shafts in place of the levers, then notice how many revolutions the input shaft makes while the output shaft makes one revolution. The velocity ratio will then be :

$$\frac{\text{Revolutions of input shaft}}{\text{Revolutions of output shaft in the same time.}}$$

In both cases the velocity ratio can be obtained without any load being applied. *The velocity ratio depends only on the arrangement of the machine.* After the machine has been made the velocity ratio could be determined and its value stamped on the nameplate. It would remain constant provided there was no change in the arrangement of the machine. This is not the case with the mechanical advantage as we shall see later.

Now consider the work which is done by the effort and on the load in the machine shown in Fig. 54.

Work done by effort $= \text{force} \times \text{distance} = Px$

Work done in lifting load $= \text{force} \times \text{distance} = Wh$

$$\text{Efficiency of machine} = \frac{\text{work done in moving load}}{\text{work done by the effort}}$$

$$= \frac{Wh}{Px}$$

$$= \frac{\dfrac{W}{P}}{\dfrac{x}{h}}$$

$$\therefore \text{Efficiency} = \frac{\text{mechanical advantage}}{\text{velocity ratio}}$$

Usually efficiency is expressed as a percentage and therefore the value obtained in the above calculation should be multiplied by 100 to give percentage.

If the machine were perfect, and no work had to be done in overcoming friction and lifting additional weights in the form of levers and hooks, then we could expect that the work done by the effort would be equal to the work done in moving the load. This would give an efficiency of 1 or 100 per cent. and this in turn would meant that:

$$\frac{\text{Mechanical advantage}}{\text{Velocity ratio}} = 1 \text{ for the perfect machine.}$$

In other words, *in the perfect machine the mechanical advantage is equal to the velocity ratio.*

Consider the machine in Fig. 54 to be perfect. This would mean that we should require a smaller effort to lift the same load, because there is no friction to overcome. Let us call this effort the ideal effort and represent it by I.

$$\text{Mechanical advantage for the perfect machine} = \frac{W}{I}$$

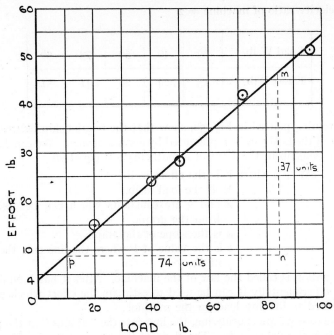

FIG. 56—LOAD–EFFORT GRAPH

Velocity ratio = mechanical advantage for perfect machine.

$\therefore$ velocity ratio $= \dfrac{W}{I}$

Ideal effort I $= \dfrac{\text{load}}{\text{velocity ratio}}$

Substituting this expression into that which we have obtained for the general machine we have:

$$\text{Efficiency} = \frac{\text{mechanical advantage}}{\text{velocity ratio}}$$

$$= \frac{\dfrac{W}{P}}{\dfrac{W}{I}} = \frac{I}{P}$$

$$\text{Efficiency} = \frac{\text{ideal effort}}{\text{actual effort.}}$$

The Law of a Machine

If we carry out an experiment on a machine to find the effort required to overcome various loads, the results that we should obtain would be similar to the following:

Velocity ratio of machine = 2

Load W lb. . .	20	40	50	72	96
Effort P lb. . .	15	24	28	41	51

These results, plotted in Fig. 56, show that the relationship between the effort and the load can be represented by a straight line. We can express this relationship in the form of a mathematical equation :

$P = aW + b$ where P is the effort in lb.

W is the load in lb.

a and b are constants which can be obtained from the graph.

a is the slope of the graph.

b is the value of P where the line cuts the axis of P.

This equation is called the law of the machine. After it has been determined experimentally it can be used to estimate the effort which would be required to lift any load on the machine.

In the case we are considering, the line cuts the " P axis " at the point 4. This is the value of b. The slope of the line is given by $\frac{mn}{pn}$ where m and p are any points on the line, mn and pn being vertical and horizontal lines.

From the graph $mn = 37$

$pn = 74$

slope of line $= \dfrac{37}{74} = 0.5$. This is the value of a.

The law of the machine is $P = 0.5 W + 4$.

To move a load of 200 lb. the required effort is given by

$$P = (0.5 \times 200) + 4$$
$$= 104 \text{ lb.}$$

Variation of Efficiency

The velocity ratio of a machine is constant and cannot be altered without making a change to the arrangement of the machine. The mechanical advantage of the machine varies with the applied load. In the results just quoted, we find that the mechanical advantage was 1·33 when the load was 20 lb. When the load was 96 lb. the mechanical advantage increased to 1·88. Since efficiency is found by dividing mechanical advantage by velocity ratio, it follows that efficiency will depend upon load. The efficiency of a machine is not constant ; it will generally be found to increase with increase of load.

The mechanical advantage and the efficiency of the machine used in the above test are tabulated below and plotted in Fig. 57.

Load lb.	20	40	50	72	96
Effort lb.	15	24	28	41	51
Mechanical Advantage ..	1·33	1·66	1·76	1·78	1·88
Mechanical Efficiency ..	0·67	0·83	0·88	0·89	0·94

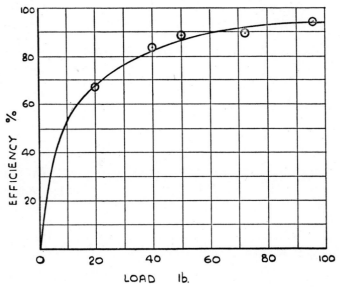

FIG. 57—LOAD–EFFICIENCY GRAPH
The efficiency of a machine is not constant but increases as the load increases.

With the smaller loads there is a considerable increase in efficiency for a corresponding increase in load. Gradually the curve flattens out, showing that further increases in load produce only small changes in the efficiency.

Example 36.—In a certain lifting machine an effort of 20 lb. is required to lift a load of 180 lb. It is found that the effort has to move a distance of 2 ft. 6 in. while the load moves 2 in. Find :

(a) work done in lifting load 1 ft.,
(b) distance moved by effort while load moves 1 ft.,

(c) work done by the effort while the load is moving 1 ft.,

(d) efficiency of the machine,

(e) effort required to lift the 180 lb. load if the machine were perfect.

(a) Work done in lifting 180 lb. 1 ft. = force × distance
$$= 180 \times 1$$
$$= 180 \text{ ft. lb.} \quad \textbf{Ans.}$$

(b) Velocity ratio $= \dfrac{\text{distance moved by effort}}{\text{distance moved by load}} = \dfrac{30 \text{ in.}}{2 \text{ in.}} = 15$

in same time

i.e., effort moves 15 times distance moved by load in same time. Distance moved by effort while load moves 1 ft. = 15 × 1
$$= 15 \text{ ft.} \quad \textbf{Ans.}$$

(c) Work done by effort = force × distance
$$= 20 \times 15$$
$$= 300 \text{ ft. lb.} \quad \textbf{Ans.}$$

(d) Efficiency of machine $= \dfrac{\text{work done in lifting load}}{\text{work done by effort in same time}}$

$$= \dfrac{180}{300}$$

$$= 0\cdot6 \text{ or } 60\%. \quad \textbf{Ans.}$$

(e) Efficiency $= \dfrac{\text{ideal effort}}{\text{actual effort}}$

$$\therefore 0\cdot6 = \dfrac{1}{20} \qquad \therefore \text{ ideal effort} = 20 \times 0\cdot6$$
$$= 12 \text{ lb.} \quad \textbf{Ans.}$$

NOTE 1.—The ideal effort is 12 lb. and the actual effort is 20 lb. This means that 8 lb. is required to overcome friction forces and also to lift the hook and pulley block. This is the reason for the low efficiency of 60%.

2. The mechanical advantage of the machine when raising 180 lb. is equal to $\dfrac{180}{20} = 9$. We could have used this figure to find the efficiency because efficiency $= \dfrac{\text{mechanical advantage}}{\text{velocity ratio}}$

$$= \dfrac{9}{15} = 0\cdot6$$

This provides a useful check on the method used above.

Example 37.—A winch is used to draw a cable through an underground conduit. The winch is designed so that the effort moves through a distance of 12 ft. whilst the cable is moved 4 in.

(i) What effort would be required to produce a force of 504 lb. on the cable if the winch were frictionless?

(ii) If the actual effort required is 20 lb. what is the efficiency of the machine ?

(iii) If by oiling the winch, the efficiency is increased by 10% what effort would then be required to produce the same force on the cable ?

$$\text{Velocity ratio} = \frac{\text{distance moved by effort}}{\text{distance moved by load in same time}}$$

$$= \frac{12 \times 12}{4} \quad \text{(convert both to inches)}$$

$$= 36$$

(i) $\text{Ideal effort} = \dfrac{\text{load}}{\text{velocity ratio}} \quad \text{(for perfect machine)}$

$$= \frac{504}{36}$$

$$= 14 \text{ lb. Ans.}$$

(ii) $\text{Efficiency} = \dfrac{\text{ideal effort}}{\text{actual effort}}$

$$= \frac{14}{20} = 0 \cdot 7 \text{ or } 70\%. \quad \text{Ans.}$$

(iii) New efficiency $= 70\% + 10\% = 80\%$ or $0 \cdot 8$

$$\text{Actual effort} = \frac{\text{ideal effort}}{\text{efficiency}}$$

$$= \frac{14}{0 \cdot 8} = 17 \cdot 5 \text{ lb. Ans.}$$

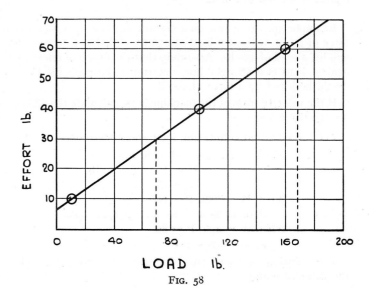

FIG. 58

Example 38.—The law of a machine as taken from a load-effort graph is $W = 3P - 20$ where W and P are in pounds.

Draw the graph and find:

(a) the effort required to lift a load of $1\frac{1}{2}$ cwt.,
(b) the load lifted by an effort of 30 lb.,
(c) the effort required to operate the machine at no-load.

The graph will be a straight line so that we shall require only three points in order to draw it. (The third point is taken as a check on the other two.)

$$\text{Let } P = \text{10 lb. then } W = (3 \times 10) - 20$$
$$= \text{10 lb.}$$
$$P = \text{60 lb. then } W = (3 \times 60) - 20$$
$$= \text{160 lb.}$$
$$P = \text{40 lb. then } W = (3 \times 40) - 20$$
$$= \text{100 lb.}$$

Using these three values we can draw the graph. (Fig. 58.) From the graph the answers to (a), (b), and (c) can be obtained. Effort required to lift load of $1\frac{1}{2}$ cwt. or 168 lb. is 62·6 lb. Load lifted by effort of 30 lb. is 70 lb.

Effort required to operate machine at no-load (i.e., when $W = 0$) is 6·6 lb.

These values may also be obtained by substituting in the equation for the machine.

Example 39.—In a test on a certain machine it is found that a force of 60 lb. will lift a load of 256 lb. and that a force of 80 lb. will lift a load of 420 lb. Assuming that the graph of effort plotted against load is a straight line, determine the probable load that would be lifted by a force of 200 lb.

If the velocity ratio of the machine is 15, calculate the efficiencies for the three loads.

Let the equation connecting load and effort be:

$$P = aW + b \text{ where } a \text{ and } b \text{ are constants.}$$
$$P = \text{the effort in lb.}$$
$$W = \text{the load in lb.}$$
$$\text{When } W = 256, P = 60$$
$$\therefore 60 = 256a + b \quad \dots\dots\dots\dots(1)$$
$$\text{When } W = 420, P = 80$$
$$\therefore 80 = 420a + b \quad \dots\dots\dots\dots(2)$$

The solution of these two simultaneous equations will give the value of a and b.

Subtract (1) from (2) :

$$80 = 420a + b$$
$$60 = 256a + b$$
$$\overline{20 = 164a}$$

$$a = \frac{20}{164} = \frac{1}{8 \cdot 2}$$

Substitute this value in equation (1) :

$$60 = (256 \times \frac{1}{8 \cdot 2}) + b$$
$$60 = 31 \cdot 2 + b$$
$$b = 28 \cdot 8$$

Law of machine is P $= \dfrac{W}{8 \cdot 2} + 28 \cdot 8$

This can be written $\quad W = 8 \cdot 2(P - 28 \cdot 8)$

When the effort P is 200 the probable load will be :

$$W = 8 \cdot 2(200 - 28 \cdot 8)$$
$$= 8 \cdot 2 \times 171 \cdot 2$$
$$= \mathbf{1405 \ lb. \ \ Ans.}$$

$$\text{Efficiency} \quad = \frac{\text{mechanical advantage}}{\text{velocity ratio}}$$

$$= \frac{W}{P \times \text{velocity ratio}}.$$

When load is 256 lb., effort is 60 lb.

$$\text{Efficiency} \quad = \frac{256}{60 \times 15} = 0 \cdot 284$$
$$= 28 \cdot 4 \%.$$

When load is 420 lb., effort is 80 lb.

$$\text{Efficiency} \quad = \frac{420}{80 \times 15} = 0 \cdot 35$$
$$= 35 \%.$$

When effort is 200 lb., load is 1405 lb.

$$\text{Efficiency} \quad = \frac{1405}{200 \times 15} = 0 \cdot 468$$
$$= 46 \cdot 8 \%.$$

Load lb.	..	256	420	1405	
Efficiency %	..	28·4	35	46·8	**Ans.**

The Lever

We shall now apply the foregoing principles to various machines, the simplest of which is the lever.

The lever, shown in Fig. 59, is arranged with the fulcrum F between the load W and the effort P. Assuming that the lever is a perfect machine, i.e., the lever has no weight and there are no friction forces acting

at the fulcrum or the points of application of the load and effort, we
can find the relationship between the load and the effort by taking
moments about the fulcrum.

$$Px = Wh$$

$$\text{Mechanical advantage} = \frac{\text{load}}{\text{effort}} = \frac{W}{P}$$

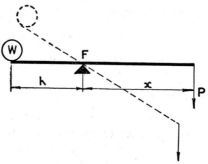

FIG. 59—SIMPLE LEVER
Fulcrum between the load and the effort.

In a perfect machine the velocity ratio is equal to the mechanical
advantage.

$$\text{Velocity ratio} = \frac{W}{P} = \frac{x}{h}$$

In practice, for a given load, P will be greater than the value given by
the equation $Px = Wh$. The velocity ratio, however, will always be $\frac{x}{h}$.

Example 40.—A lever of the type shown in Fig. 59 is 24 in.
long and is mounted on a pivot 8 in. from one end. An effort
of 8 lb. is applied at the end of the longer arm to overcome a load
of 15 lb. acting at the other end.   What is the velocity ratio,
mechanical advantage, and the efficiency of the lever? If the
lever were mounted on a frictionless pivot what effort would be
required to lift the load?

$$\text{Velocity ratio } \frac{x}{h} = \frac{16}{8} = 2$$

$$\text{Mechanical advantage} = \frac{\text{load}}{\text{effort}} = \frac{15}{8} = 1 \cdot 875$$

$$\text{Efficiency} = \frac{\text{mechanical advantage}}{\text{velocity ratio}} = \frac{1 \cdot 875}{2}$$

$$= 0 \cdot 9375 \text{ or } 93\tfrac{3}{4}\%. \quad \textbf{Ans.}$$

In a perfect machine mechanical advantage = velocity ratio
∴ Mechanical advantage = 2.   **Ans.**

$$\text{Effort} = \frac{\text{load}}{\text{mechanical advantage}} = \frac{15}{2} = 7\tfrac{1}{2} \text{ lb. } \textbf{Ans.}$$

Note that this would be obtained by taking moments about F.

$$P \times 16 = 15 \times 8$$

$$P = \frac{15 \times 8}{16} = 7\frac{1}{2}\,\text{lb.}$$

Alternative Lever Arrangements

In the type shown in Fig. 60 the load W is applied between the effort P and the fulcrum F.

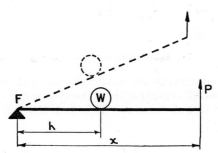

FIG. 60—SIMPLE LEVER
Load between the fulcrum and the effort.

The velocity ratio is again x/h where both distances are measured from the fulcrum.

Bell Crank Levers

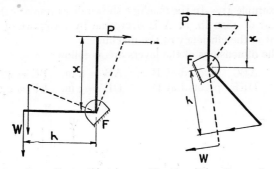

FIG 61.—BELL CRANK LEVER   FIG. 62—BELL CRANK LEVER

A lever which is bent as shown in Fig. 61 and Fig. 62 is called a bell crank lever. It is used to provide a change in the direction of the applied forces.

Again the velocity ratio is x/h.

Note that in all the cases considered x and h are the *perpendicular* distances from the fulcrum to the line of action of the effort and load.

Combination of Levers

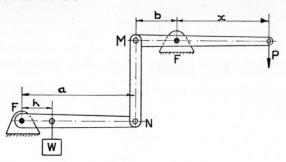

FIG. 63—COMBINATION OF LEVERS

Two lever arrangements are connected together by the link MN. (Fig. 63.) The overall velocity ratio of the system can be found by considering W to move a distance d. Then link MN will move through a distance given by:

$$d \times \frac{a}{h}$$

and P will move a distance of $d \times \frac{a}{h} \times \frac{x}{b}$

Overall velocity ratio is therefore $\frac{a}{h} \times \frac{x}{b}$

which is equal to the product of the velocity ratios of the separate levers.

Example 41.—In the machine shown diagrammatically in Fig. 64 a load of 4800 lb. at A is overcome by an effort of 3 lb. at M. What is the efficiency of the machine?

The dimensions of the levers are as follow:

ABC   pivoted at B   AB = 2 in.   BC = 40 in.
DEF   pivoted at D   DE = 3 in.   EF = 27 in.

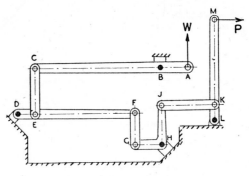

FIG. 64

GHJ pivoted at H   GH = 8 in.   HJ = 16 in.
LKM pivoted at L   LK = 3 in.   LM = 18 in.

Lever ABC   Velocity ratio $= \dfrac{40}{2} = 20$

  DEF   „   „ $= \dfrac{27 + 3}{3} = \dfrac{30}{3} = 10$

  GHJ   „   „ $= \dfrac{16}{8} = 2$

  LKM   „   „ $= \dfrac{18}{3} = 6$

Overall velocity ratio $= 20 \times 10 \times 2 \times 6$
                         $= 2400$

Mechanical advantage $= \dfrac{\text{load}}{\text{effort}} = \dfrac{4800}{3} = 1600$

Efficiency of machine $= \dfrac{\text{mech. adv.}}{\text{vel. ratio}} = \dfrac{1600}{2400} = \tfrac{2}{3}$

                        $= 66\tfrac{2}{3}\%.$ **Ans.**

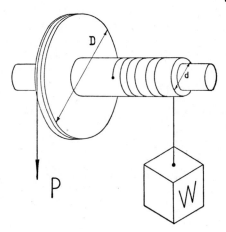

FIG. 65—WHEEL

Wheel and Axle (Fig. 65)

The load is raised by a cord wrapped around the axle whose diameter is d. The diameter D of the wheel is larger than that of the axle to which it is rigidly connected. The effort is applied to a cord wrapped round the wheel. The whole arrangement is mounted in bearings.

When the wheel and axle make one revolution, a length of cord equal to πd is wound on to the axle, i.e., the load is raised through a distance πd. Similarly the effort moves through a distance πD. The effort will, of course, move away from the wheel.

$$\text{Hence velocity ratio} = \frac{\text{distance moved by effort}}{\text{distance moved by load in same time}}$$

$$= \frac{\pi D}{\pi d}$$

$$= \frac{D}{d}$$

$$\text{Mechanical efficiency} = \frac{\text{work done in lifting load}}{\text{work done by effort in same time}}$$

$$= \frac{\pi d \times W}{\pi D \times P}$$

$$= \frac{W d}{PD}.$$

Example 42.—A wheel and axle are used for raising water from a well. The diameter of the axle is 10 in. and the crank is 2 ft. long. An effort of 30 lb. is required to raise a load of 100 lb. What is the mechanical efficiency of the arrangement?

$$\text{Velocity ratio} = \frac{\text{distance moved by effort}}{\text{distance moved by load in same time}}$$

$$= \frac{2\pi \times 24}{\pi \times 10} \qquad \begin{array}{l}\text{Since equivalent diameter of} \\ \text{the wheel would be twice} \\ \text{radius of crank} = 2 \times 24 \text{ in.}\end{array}$$

$$= 4\cdot8$$

$$\text{Mechanical advantage} = \frac{\text{load}}{\text{effort}} = \frac{100}{30} = 3\tfrac{1}{3}$$

$$\text{Mechanical efficiency} = \frac{MA}{VR} = \frac{3\tfrac{1}{3}}{4\cdot8} = 0\cdot694 \text{ or } 69\cdot4\%. \quad \textbf{Ans.}$$

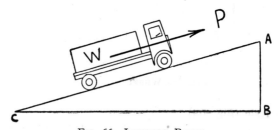

FIG. 66—INCLINED PLANE

The lorry is in effect lifted through a vertical height AB. The tractive force moving the lorry up the plane is P acting parallel to the plane.

The Inclined Plane

The inclined plane was one of the earliest machines used by man. It was found much easier to raise a load by moving it up an incline than by lifting it through a vertical height.

The effort P moves through a distance AC while the load W moves through a vertical distance equal to AB. (Notice that distances must always be measured in the direction in which the force acts. The weight of the load acts vertically downwards.)

Velocity ratio $= \dfrac{\text{distance moved by effort}}{\text{distance moved by load in same time}}$

$= \dfrac{AC}{AB}$

Mechanical advantage $= \dfrac{\text{load}}{\text{effort}} = \dfrac{W}{P}$

Mechanical efficiency $= \dfrac{\text{work done in lifting load}}{\text{work done by effort in same time}}$

$= \dfrac{W \times AB}{P \times AC}$

Example 43.—Find the mechanical advantage and velocity ratio of a perfectly smooth inclined plane when a force of 28 lb. parallel to the plane is sufficient to push a weight of 2 cwt. up the plane with uniform velocity. If the surface of the plane became roughened so that the applied force had to be increased to 40 lb., what would then be the mechanical advantage, the velocity ratio, and the efficiency of the plane?   U.L.C.I.

(*a*) The mechanical advantage $= \dfrac{\text{load}}{\text{effort}} = \dfrac{2 \times 112}{28} = 8.$

Since the plane is perfectly smooth it can be considered to be a perfect machine whose efficiency is 100%. In such a case the velocity ratio is equal to the mechanical advantage.

∴ velocity ratio = 8

(*b*) When surface is rough.

Mechanical advantage $= \dfrac{\text{load}}{\text{effort}} = \dfrac{2 \times 112}{40} = 5\cdot6$

The velocity ratio will still be 8, since it is unaffected by the roughness of the plane. It only depends upon the angle of the plane.

Mechanical efficiency $= \dfrac{\text{mechanical advantage}}{\text{velocity ratio}}$

$= \dfrac{5\cdot6}{8}$

$= 0\cdot7 \text{ or } 70\%$

Case (a)   Mechanical advantage   = 8
Velocity ratio   = 8
Mechanical efficiency   = 100%

(b)   Mechanical advantage   = 5·6
Velocity ratio   = 8
Mechanical efficiency   = 70%   **Ans.**

Screw Jack

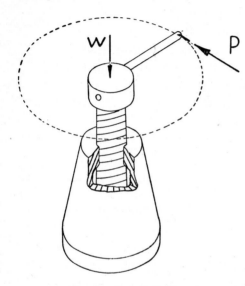

FIG. 67—SCREW JACK
The effort is applied at the end of the arm, length
r. For each revolution of the arm the load is
raised by an amount equal to the lead of the
screw.

Fig. 67 shows diagrammatically the arrangement of a simple screw jack. The three essential parts are :

(1) The screw, usually single start, provided with a collar at its upper end in which are drilled "tommy holes." There is also a cap at the end of the screw which is arranged so that it does not rotate with the screw. The load is taken by the cap.

(2) The main body of the jack into which the screw is screwed.

(3) The lever fitted into one of the tommy holes in the upper part of the screw.

Generally the screw is used to lift loads so that the screw axis is vertical and the lever moves in a horizontal plane. The effort is applied at the end of the lever in a direction perpendicular to its length.

When the screw makes one revolution the effort moves through a distance of $2\pi r$ where r is the length of the lever. The load moves through a vertical distance equal to the lead of the screw, l which in the case of a single start thread is equal to the pitch of the screw.

$$\text{Velocity ratio} = \frac{\text{distance moved by effort}}{\text{distance moved by load in same time}}$$

$$= \frac{2\pi r}{l}$$

Mechanical advantage $= \dfrac{\text{load}}{\text{effort}}$

$= \dfrac{W}{P}$

Mechanical efficiency $= \dfrac{\text{work done in lifting load}}{\text{word done by effort in same time}}$

$= \dfrac{Wl}{2\pi rP}.$

Example 44.—A screw jack is operated by a bar pushed through a hole in the spindle. The pitch of the screw is $\frac{1}{2}$ in. A force of 60 lb. applied at right angles to the bar, at a radius of 14 in. from the axis of the screw, is found to lift a casting weighing 2 tons which rests upon the top of the jack. Find the velocity ratio, the mechanical advantage, and the mechanical efficiency of the machine under these conditions. U.E.I.

When the screw makes 1 revolution :
the effort moves $2\pi \times 14$ in.
the load moves $\frac{1}{2}$ in.

Velocity ratio $= \dfrac{\text{distance moved by effort}}{\text{distance moved by load in same time}}$

$= \dfrac{2\pi \times 14}{\frac{1}{2}}$ $\left(\pi = \dfrac{22}{7}\right)$

$= 176.$ **Ans.**

Mechanical advantage $= \dfrac{\text{load}}{\text{effort}}$

$= \dfrac{2 \times 2240}{60}$

$= 74\frac{2}{3}.$ **Ans.**

Mechanical efficiency $= \dfrac{\text{work done in moving load}}{\text{work done by effort in same time}}$

$= \dfrac{2 \times 2240 \times \frac{1}{2}}{2\pi \times 14 \times 60}$

$= 0{\cdot}425$ or $42{\cdot}5\%.$ **Ans.**

Alternatively :

Mechanical efficiency $= \dfrac{\text{mechanical advantage}}{\text{velocity ratio}}$

$= \dfrac{74\frac{2}{3}}{176}$

$= 0{\cdot}425$ or $42{\cdot}5\%.$ **Ans.**

Gear Drives (Fig. 68)

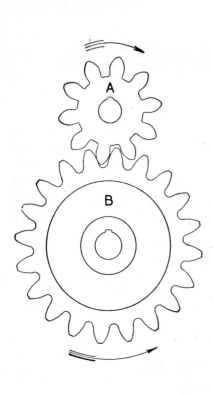

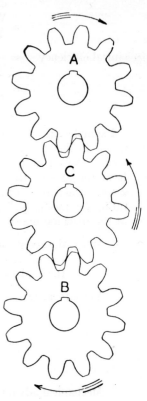

FIG. 68—SPUR GEAR DRIVE

FIG. 69—SPUR GEAR DRIVE
The idler wheel C has the effect of
making A and B rotate in the
same direction without altering
the velocity ratio of the drive.

In a gear wheel a number of specially shaped projections or " teeth"
are produced on the periphery of the wheel. These teeth mesh with
corresponding teeth on a second wheel so that motion can be transferred
from one to the other without any slip taking place.

Two wheels A and B are geared together so that wheel A is driving
wheel B in the opposite direction to A. Let the number of teeth in
wheel A be a and in wheel B be b. The point on the line joining
the centres of the wheels at which the gears mesh is called the pitch
point P. Now in any interval of time the same number of teeth will
pass point P whether we think of wheel A or B. Suppose in a given

interval of time t teeth pass point P. This means that A has made $\frac{t}{a}$ revolutions and B has made $\frac{t}{b}$ revolutions in the same time. The velocity ratio of the drive is:

$$\frac{\text{Revolutions of driver wheel (the effort)}}{\text{Revolutions of driven wheel (the load) in same time}}$$

$$= \frac{\dfrac{t}{a}}{\dfrac{t}{b}}$$

$$= \frac{b}{a}$$

$$= \frac{\text{number of teeth in driven wheel}}{\text{number of teeth in driver wheel}}.$$

If we required to know the speed of the driven wheel we can apply the relationship:

$$\frac{\text{R.p.m. driver}}{\text{R.p.m. driven}} = \frac{\text{teeth in driven}}{\text{teeth in driver}}$$

$$\text{R.p.m. driven wheel} = \frac{\text{teeth in driver}}{\text{teeth in driven}} \times \text{r.p.m. driver.}$$

Use of the Idler Wheel (Fig. 69)

A third wheel C, known as an idler wheel, is sometimes inserted between A and B. The effect of this is to make wheel B rotate in the same direction as that of wheel A, although the speed of B is not affected by the insertion of C.

Let the teeth in the wheels A, B, and C be denoted by a, b, and c respectively.

$$\text{R.p.m. of C} = \frac{a}{c} \times \text{r.p.m. of A}$$

$$\text{R.p.m. of B} = \frac{c}{b} \times \text{r.p.m. of C.}$$

$$= \frac{c}{b} \times \frac{a}{c} \times \text{r.p.m. of A}$$

$$= \frac{a}{b} \times \text{r.p.m. of A.}$$

Example 45.—Fig. 70 shows the gear drive in a certain machine tool. If shaft A rotates at 900 r.p.m. what is the speed of shaft K ?

$$\text{Speed of C} = \text{speed of B} \times \frac{B}{C}$$

$$= 900 \times \frac{40}{60}$$

$$= 600 \text{ r.p.m., which is also the speed of D.}$$

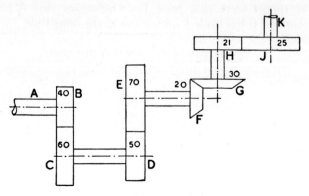

Fig. 70

Speed of E = speed of D $\times \dfrac{D}{E}$

$= 600 \times \dfrac{50}{70}$

$= 428\tfrac{4}{7}$ r.p.m., which is also the speed of F.

Speed of G = speed of F $\times \dfrac{F}{G}$

$= 428\tfrac{4}{7} \times \dfrac{20}{30}$

$= 285\tfrac{5}{7}$ r.p.m., which is also the speed of H.

Speed of K = speed of H $\times \dfrac{H}{J}$

$= 285\tfrac{5}{7} \times \dfrac{21}{25}$

$= 240$ r.p.m.

A question of this type can be solved by a continuous calculation, taking the wheels in order and starting from A.

Speed of K = speed of A $\times \dfrac{B}{C} \times \dfrac{D}{E} \times \dfrac{F}{G} \times \dfrac{H}{J}$

$= 900 \times \dfrac{40}{60} \times \dfrac{50}{70} \times \dfrac{20}{30} \times \dfrac{21}{25}$

$= $ **240 r.p.m. Ans.**

Example 46.—State clearly what is meant by the following terms applied to a lifting machine : (*a*) mechanical advantage ; (*b*) velocity ratio. A single geared winch has a wheel of 20 teeth on the driving spindle, gearing with a 50-tooth wheel on the drum spindle. The drum is 8 in. diameter. The driving spindle is turned by means of a handle on which the effort acts at a distance from the centre of that spindle. Neglecting the diameter of the rope on the drum and the effect of friction, determine the velocity ratio and the mechanical advantage of the machine. What force would be required at the handle to raise a load of 300 lb. suspended from the drum under these conditions?

N.C.T.E.C.

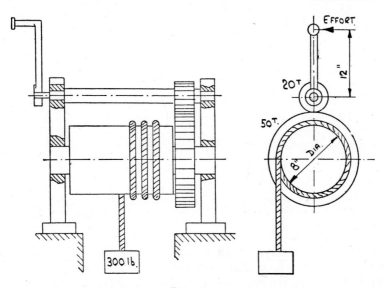

FIG. 71

A diagram of the arrangement is shown in Fig. 71.

Let the driving spindle make 1 revolution anticlockwise in the view shown in Fig. 71.

The effort at the end of the handle moves a distance equal to $2\pi \times 12 = 24\pi$ inches.

The drum makes $1 \times \dfrac{20}{50} = 0\cdot4$ revolutions clockwise.

And thus the load is lifted by $0\cdot4 \times 8\pi$ in. $= 3\cdot2\pi$ in. (one turn of the drum would lift the load 8π in., therefore $0\cdot4$ turns will lift it $0\cdot4 \times 8\pi$).

$$\text{Velocity ratio} \;=\; \frac{\text{distance moved by effort}}{\text{distance moved by load in same time}}$$

$$=\; \frac{24\pi}{3\cdot2\pi}$$

Velocity ratio $= 7\tfrac{1}{2}$ **Ans.**

Since the machine is considered frictionless the mechanical advantage equals the velocity ratio.

$\therefore$ mechanical advantage $= 7\frac{1}{2}$

$$\frac{\text{Load}}{\text{Effort}} = 7\frac{1}{2}$$

$\therefore$ effort $= \dfrac{\text{load}}{7\frac{1}{2}} = \dfrac{300}{7\frac{1}{2}} = 40$ lb. **Ans.**

Velocity ratio $= 7\frac{1}{2}$; mechanical advantage $= 7\frac{1}{2}$; effort $= 40$ lb. **Ans.**

Belt and Chain Drives

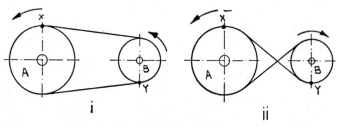

i   ii

FIG. 72—BELT DRIVE
The open belt drive shown in (i) is arranged so that A and B rotate in the same direction. If the belt is crossed as in (ii) the wheels rotate in opposite directions.

Consider two pulleys A and B, connecting which is an endless belt. A is the driving wheel. It is assumed that no slip takes place between the belt and the pulleys. When A makes N revolutions the point X on the rim of A moves through a distance of $N\pi d_a$. In moving round, a length of belt equal to $N\pi d_a$ is moved from right to left and this in turn causes a point Y on the rim of wheel B to move through a distance of $N\pi d_a$.

Number of revolutions made by wheel B $= \dfrac{N\pi d_a}{\text{circumference of B}}$

$= \dfrac{N\pi d_a}{\pi d_b}$

$= \dfrac{\text{dia. of A}}{\text{dia. of B}} \times N$

$\therefore$ speed of B $=$ speed of A $\times \dfrac{\text{dia. of A}}{\text{dia. of B}}$.

If the belt is "open," as shown in Fig. 72 (i), both wheels rotate in the same direction. If the belt is "crossed," as shown in Fig. 72 (ii), the wheels rotate in opposite directions.

The chain drive is similar to the belt drive with the exception that the motion is transmitted much more positively. The chain cannot slip around the wheels or sprockets as they are usually called. The rollers in the chain fit into specially shaped teeth cut in the sprockets.

$$\text{Speed of B} = \text{speed of A} \times \frac{\text{dia. of A}}{\text{dia. of B}}$$

and since the number of teeth in the sprockets is proportional to the diameter of the sprockets we can write:

$$\text{Speed of B} = \text{speed of A} \times \frac{\text{teeth in A}}{\text{teeth in B}}$$

The chain drive is always "open," i.e., the two sprocket wheels always rotate in the same direction.

Example 47.—The line shaft in a machine shop is driven at 150 r.p.m. For a certain lathe the pulley on the line shaft is 20 in. diameter and that on the countershaft is 15 in. diameter. The speed cone on the countershaft has four steps of the following diameters, 16 in., 12 in., 8 in., and 4 in. The speed cone of the lathe has the following diameters, 6 in., 10 in., 14 in., and 18 in.

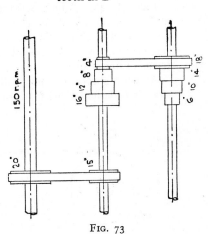

FIG. 73

Determine the available speeds of the lathe (Fig. 73).

$$\text{Speed of countershaft} = \text{speed of line shaft} \times \frac{\text{driving pulley}}{\text{driven pulley}}$$

$$= 150 \times \frac{20}{15}$$

$$= 200 \text{ r.p.m.}$$

Top Speed of Lathe. This occurs when the belt is round the 16 in. and 6 in. pulleys.

$$\text{Speed} = \text{speed of line shaft} \times \frac{\text{driving pulley}}{\text{driven pulley}}$$

$$= 200 \times \frac{16}{6}$$

$$= 533\tfrac{1}{3} \text{ r.p.m.}$$

2nd Speed. Belt around 12 in. and 10 in. pulleys.

$$\text{Speed} = 200 \times \frac{12}{10}$$

$$= 240 \text{ r.p.m.}$$

3rd Speed. Belt around 8 in. and 14 in. pulleys.

$$\text{Speed} = 200 \times \frac{8}{14}$$

$$= 114\cdot3 \text{ r.p.m.}$$

Low Speed.   Belt around 4 in. and 18 in. pulleys.

$$\text{Speed} = 200 \times \frac{4}{18}$$

$$= 44 \cdot 4 \text{ r.p.m.}$$

Lathe speeds are $533\frac{1}{3}$, 240, 114·3, and 44·4 r.p.m.   **Ans.**

Example 48.—A bicycle drive has 48 teeth on the crank sprocket and 16 on the wheel sprocket. The cranks are 8 in. long and the road wheel is 26 in. diameter. What is the velocity ratio of the road-wheel rim to the pedal (*a*) in terms of revolutions? (*b*) in terms of linear speed?

At what speed in m.p.h. will the bicycle be moving when the rider is pedalling at 60 turns of the crank per min.?

N.C.T.E.C.

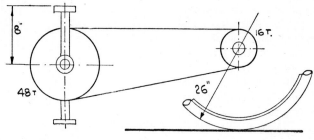

Fig. 74

When crank makes 1 revolution the road wheel makes $\frac{48}{16} = 3$ revolutions.

∴ velocity ratio (in terms of revolutions) = 3.   **Ans.**

During one revolution the crank travels $2\pi \times 8 = 16\pi$ in. In the same time the road wheel makes 3 revolutions and a point on the rim travels $3 \times \pi \times 26 = 78\pi$ in.

∴ velocity ratio (in terms of linear speed) $= \frac{78\pi}{16\pi} = 4\frac{7}{8}$.   **Ans.**

When pedalling at 60 turns per min. the road wheel is making $3 \times 60 = 180$ r.p.m.

$$\text{Linear speed} = \frac{180 \times 26\pi}{12} \text{ ft. per min.}$$

$$= \frac{180 \times 26\pi}{12 \times 5280} \text{ miles per min.}$$

$$= \frac{180 \times 26\pi \times 60}{12 \times 5280} \text{ m.p.h.}$$

$$= 13 \cdot 9 \text{ m.p.h.}   \textbf{Ans.}$$

EXERCISE 6

(1) In a certain machine an effort of 30 lb. is required to lift a load of 240 lb. It is found that the effort moves a distance of 5 ft. while the load moves 6 in. Find:

    (a) work done in lifting load 1 ft.,

    (b) distance moved by effort while load moves 1 ft.,

    (c) work done by the effort while the load is moving 1 ft.,

    (d) the efficiency of the machine,

    (e) effort required to lift the 240 lb. load if the machine were perfect.

(2) In a test on a lifting machine it was found that an effort of 12 lb. was required to lift a load of 300 lb. The effort moved a distance of 10 ft. while the load moved 3 in. Find:

    (a) the work done in lifting the load 1 ft.,

    (b) the distance moved by the effort while the load is moving 1 ft.,

    (c) the work done by the effort while the load is moving 1 ft.,

    (d) the efficiency of the machine,

    (e) the effort required to lift the 300 lb. load if the machine were perfect.

(3) A machine is designed to pull a cable through an underground conduit. The machine is arranged so that the effort moves through a distance of 20 ft. while the cable is pulled through 8 in.

    (a) What effort would be required to produce a force of 900 lb. on the cable if the winch were frictionless?

    (b) If the actual effort required is 50 lb. what is the efficiency of the machine?

    (c) If by oiling the machine the efficiency is increased by 15%, what effort would then be required to produce the same force on the cable?

(4) A machine is used to move bars of steel in a stores. The effort moves through a distance of 8 ft. while the bars are pulled through 6 in.

    (a) What effort would be required to produce a force of 192 lb. on the steel bars if the machine were perfect?

    (b) If the actual effort required is 16 lb. what is the efficiency of the machine?

    (c) If by making a slight adjustment the efficiency of the machine is increased by 5% what effort would then be required to produce the same force of the bars?

(5) In a simple screw jack the pitch of the screw is $\frac{1}{2}$ in., and the length of the lever at the end of which the effort is applied is 18 in. What is the velocity ratio? If an effort of 9 lb. applied at the end of the lever lifts a load of $\frac{1}{2}$ ton, what is the efficiency?

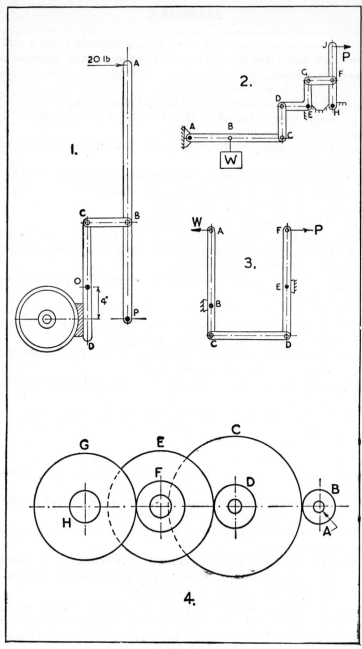

FIG. 75

(6) A simple wheel and axle has a wheel 14 in. diameter and an axle 4 in. diameter. Determine the velocity ratio of the machine and the ideal and actual efforts required to lift a load of 1 cwt. if the efficiency of the machine at this load is 80%.

(7) The following results were obtained from experiments with a certain type of lifting machine, whose velocity ratio was 25:

Load lb.	..	0	5	10	15
Effort lb.	..	0·094	0·45	0·81	1·17

Find the efficiency of the machine when lifting a load of 8 lb.

(8) Define " the moment " of a force.

A brake mechanism, as shown in Fig. 75 (1), operates with a horizontal pull of 20 lb. at A. The levers AP and CD turn about P and O respectively. AP = 36 in. ; PB = 12 in. ; OC = 12 in. Calculate the force acting on the wheel at D.   U.E.I.

(9) In the mechanism shown in Fig. 75 (2) an effort of 30 lb. applied at J overcomes a load of 90 lb. at B. The various levers are pivoted at A, E, and H. AB = 4 in. ; BC = 12 in. ; DE = 4 in. ; EG = 6 in. ; HF = 3 in. ; FJ = 9 in. Determine the efficiency of the machine.

(10) The efficiency of the machine shown in Fig. 75 (3) is 80%. The levers are pivoted about points B and E. What effort will be required at F to overcome a load of 160 lb. at A? AB = 20 in. ; BC = 8 in. ; DE = 12 in. ; EF = 16 in.

(11) Fig. 75 (4) shows the gearing of a machine tool. A is the motor shaft which runs at 480 r.p.m. The numbers of the teeth in the wheels are as follows : B 20, C 80, D 25, E 75, F 20, G 60. G is keyed to shaft H. Determine the speed of shaft H.   U.L.C.I.

(12) A hydraulic lifting mechanism on a tipping wagon lifts a load of 2 tons through a distance of 6 in. whilst the effort moves 60 ft. Calculate (a) the velocity ratio, (b) the ideal effort, and (c) the actual effort needed if the efficiency of the arrangement is 75%.

(13) In a certain lifting machine when the effort moves 35 in. the load moves 1¼ in. It is found that an effort of 8 lb. is required to raise a load of 200 lb. Calculate the velocity ratio, mechanical advantage, and mechanical efficiency when raising the given load.

(14) The pedal cranks of a bicycle are 8 in. long and are connected directly to the chain wheel of diameter 8 in. which contains 48 teeth. The sprocket on the back axle contains 16 teeth and the road wheel is 26 in. diameter. How many r.p.m. must the crank be turned by the cyclist to attain a road speed of 20 m.p.h. ? If the cranks are horizontal, what is the pull in the chain when the downward force on one pedal is 40 lb. ?

(15) An effort of 40 lb. will raise a load of 840 lb. in a certain lifting machine. If the efficiency of the machine is 0·75, what is its velocity ratio ? How far must the effort move in order to lift the load a distance of 4 ft. 6 in. ?

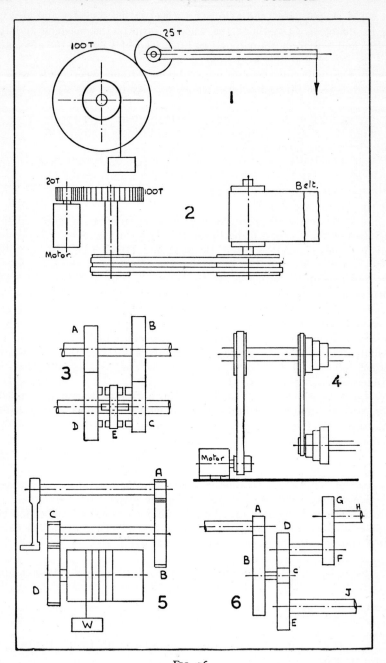

FIG. 76

(16) Fig. 76 (1) shows the outline diagram of a small lifting crab or winch. The barrel of the crab is 10 in. diameter ; the wheel on the barrel shaft has 100 teeth and the pinion on the driving shaft has 25 teeth. The machine is operated by a handle 20 in. radius and the efficiency of the machine is 80%. An effort of 40 lb. is applied at the end of the handle. Determine (a) the weight lifted, (b) the velocity ratio, and (c) the mechanical advantage.

(17) The drive to a conveyor belt is shown in Fig. 76 (2). A 20-tooth pinion on the electric motor shaft gears with a 100-tooth wheel on the intermediate shaft. At the other end of this shaft is a 15 in. diameter " V " rope pulley driving a 25 in. diameter pulley on the belt drum shaft. The belt drum is 12 in. diameter. If the motor runs at 600 r.p.m. what is the linear speed of the belt in ft. per min. ?

(18) Fig. 76 (3) gives the arrangement of a speed changing device. The upper shaft to which wheels A and B are keyed is running at 300 r.p.m. Wheels D and C run freely on the lower shaft and both are provided with clutch teeth on one side. A sliding clutch E is arranged to engage with either wheels D or C. Determine the speed of the lower shaft (a) when E engages with C, (b) when E engages with D. A has 30 teeth, B has 40, C has 25 and D has 35.

(19) In the machine tool drive shown in Fig. 76 (4) the motor runs at 1000 r.p.m. but is provided with an internal speed reducing gear so that the motor pulley runs at one fifth of the motor speed. The motor pulley, which is 8 in. diameter, drives a 12 in. diameter pulley on the countershaft. A cone pulley on the countershaft drives a similar pulley on the machine tool. Both cone pulleys have the same diameters, viz., 18 in., 15 in., 11 in., and 8 in. Determine the speed range of the machine.

(20) The arrangement of a double geared winch is shown in Fig. 76 (5). The handle 15 in. long is keyed to the driving shaft on which is fastened a 20-tooth pinion A. This gears with wheel B, 60 teeth at one end of the intermediate shaft. At the other end of the shaft is a pinion C, 25 teeth, which gears with a 65-tooth wheel on the drum shaft. The drum is 20 in. diameter. If the efficiency of the machine is 70% what effort applied at the handle will be required to lift a load of 500 lb. on the drum rope ?

(21) Fig. 76 (6) shows the gearing diagram for a price computing mechanism. Wheel A is driven at 30 r.p.m. and gears with B. Wheel B and pinion C are keyed to the same shaft. C gears with two wheels E and D. E is keyed to shaft J. Wheels D and F are keyed to the same shaft and F gears with G keyed on shaft H. The speed of J must be 0·5 1.p.m. faster than the speed of H. Determine the number of teeth required for wheel G given that the tooth numbers for the other wheels are : A 15, B 75, C 20, D 30, E 40, F 20.

(22) Find the mechanical advantage and velocity ratio of a perfectly smooth inclined plane when a force of 28 lb. parallel to the plane is sufficient to push a weight of 2 cwt. up the plane with uniform velocity. If the surface of the plane became roughened so that the applied force had to be increased to 40 lb., what would then be the mechanical advantage, the velocity ratio, and the efficiency of the plane?

U.L.C.I.

(23) The following results were obtained in an experiment with a lifting machine having a velocity ratio of 8.

Load raised lb. ..	6	10	20	30	40
Effort lb... ..	4·8	6	10	14	18

Assuming ideal conditions for the machine, calculate the loads that would be raised by the various efforts. Set out on an effort base, graphs of actual and ideal loads raised, and explain the reason for the differences between them.

U.L.C.I.

(24) What do you understand by the "velocity ratio" of a lifting machine? The length of the handle of a winch is 16 in. long and the diameter of the barrel is 8 in. The pinion on the handle axis has 16 teeth and the spur wheel on the barrel axis has 90 teeth. Find the velocity ratio of the ·winch. If the winch were without friction, what force at the handle would lift 675 lb.? In an experiment a force of 40 lb. at the handle was necessary to lift 675 lb. Account for the difference between the actual force and that necessary in a perfect machine.

U.L.C.I.

(25) Show that if two toothed wheels are in gear their speeds are inversely proportional to their diameters or their numbers of teeth.

Three spur wheels A, B, and C on parallel shafts are in gear. A has 12 teeth, B 40 teeth, and C 48 teeth. Find the speed of C when A makes 80 r.p.m. What is the purpose of wheel B?

U.L.C.I.

(26) Show the relationship between velocity ratio and mechanical advantage. Sketch and describe a wheel and axle, and obtain an expression for the velocity ratio. Explain how you would find the mechanical advantage of such a machine by experiment and state why this is less than the theoretical value obtained by experiment.

N.C.T.E.C.

(27) Describe an experiment to find the law of a lifting machine. A simple screw jack is to be designed to lift 1 ton by means of an effort of 10 lb. applied at each end of a double arm of 26 in. total length. Taking the efficiency of the jack as 0·25 find the greatest pitch of screw possible.

N.C.T.E.C.

(28) A simple winch has a handle 12 in. long which rotates a wheel having 35 teeth gearing with a wheel on the drum shaft having 150 teeth. If the diameter of the drum is 9 in. calculate the velocity ratio of the machine. Explain fully how you would obtain the velocity ratio by experiment.

N.C.T.E.C.

(29) In a hoisting machine it is found that the effort moves 2 ft. while the load rises 1½ in. Find the effort required to lift a load of 1 ton assuming an ideal frictionless machine.   N.C.T.E.C.

(30) Describe how to find the velocity ratio of a simple lifting machine. In a lifting machine a weight of 150 lb. is raised 2 in. when the effort moves 1 ft. Find the mechanical advantage of the machine assuming it to be an ideal machine and state how it would be affected by friction.
N.C.T.E.C.

(31) Define "mechanical advantage" and "velocity ratio" of a machine. A machine gave the following results :

Load lb.	0	40	80	120	160
Effort lb.	2	4·5	7·1	9·4	12

(i) Draw a graph of load against effort.
(ii) From the graph find the effort required to lift a load of 100 lb.
U.E.I.

(32) The following results were obtained from an experiment on a set of pulleys.

W denotes the weight raised and E the effort applied. Plot these results on squared paper and obtain the law connecting E and W.

W lb.	14	21	28	35	42
E lb.	2·5	3·3	4·25	5·1	6

U.E.I.

(33) The following figures were taken from a student's laboratory note book.

Results of test on screw jack :

Effort applied lb.	Load lifted lb.	Mechanical Efficiency
0·74	15	0·405
2·5	60	

Deduce the velocity ratio of the machine and fill in the omitted mechanical efficiency.   U.E.I.

CHAPTER 8

HEAT AND TEMPERATURE

In our studies so far we have considered questions such as engines pulling trains at given speeds over level tracks, cranes lifting weights, and boats moving at known speeds in known directions. We have given no thought to the way in which the power was to be produced to provide the conditions stated. The engine requires the boiler, the cylinders, and the pistons. The crane requires its motor driven by electricity, produced at the power house by an alternator driven by a turbine. The boat requires its Diesel engine with its supply of crude oil. In all these cases the motive power is supplied by an arrangement called a " Heat Engine." The heat engine makes use of the heat energy which is released when coal is burned or when petrol vapour or oil vapour is ignited. It converts this energy into another form suitable for driving machinery. Before we can understand the manner in which these engines work we must examine some of the fundamental ideas concerned with heat.

Effects of Heat

Whenever heat is applied to a substance certain effects are noticed. The following are the more important :

(1) *Change of Dimension.*—Liquids, gases, and more particularly the metal solids expand and contract when heat is added to or taken away from them.

(2) *Change of State.*—Ice melts and becomes water which will boil and be converted into steam as heat is supplied. The reverse sequence can be obtained if we remove heat in the steam. The steam will condense and the water which forms can then be frozen and ice produced.

(3) *Change of Composition.* If heat is applied to grains of sugar they will turn into a brown caramel and ultimately into a black carbon. In this case however the process is not reversible. We cannot obtain sugar from carbon merely by the process of cooling it down.

(4) *Change of Colour.* When an electric current is passed through a piece of tungsten wire, the wire becomes heated and if the current is large enough the wire will glow red and ultimately white. When we switch on the electric light this all happens instantaneously. The reason why the wire gives out a bright light is because it changes its colour due to being heated by an electric current.

(5) *Electrical Effect.*—This is perhaps the least familiar of the effects caused by heat. If two dissimilar metals such as platinum and iridium are joined together and heat is applied to the junction, a small electric current is produced which could be measured by a sensitive galvanometer. The junction of the two metals is called a thermocouple.

Temperature

In our normal conversation the words " hot " and " cold " are sufficient to describe the state of a body from a heat point of view. Scientifically, however, we must be more explicit. We must be in a position to answer the question : how hot or how cold ? We must have some method of stating the amount of hotness or coldness of a body. This is really what we mean by the temperature of a body.

Definition.—**Temperature is the degree of hotness or coldness of a body.**

It is no use relying upon our senses to tell us the temperature of a body. Think of three bowls of water, one containing cold water, another hot water, and the third lukewarm or tepid water. The right hand is placed in the hot water and the left hand in the cold water. Then if both hands are placed in the bowl of lukewarm water the right hand will experience a sensation of coldness and the left hand a sensation of hotness. We shall thus receive two different impressions of the temperature of the lukewarm water.

In order to obtain an accurate idea of the temperature we must use some scientific instrument.

We shall obtain a much more accurate idea of the temperature if we observe some of the above effects of heat. For example, if we are out of doors on a winter's evening and we see a layer of ice on the ponds we know that the temperature must be very low because ice only forms when the temperature reaches a low level. We cannot be certain of the exact temperature but we do know that it must be below a certain value. If we saw water poured on to an iron plate and the water was immediately converted into steam, then we should know that the plate was hot and that its temperature was above a certain value, although how much above we should have no means of knowing. In these two examples we are using the effect of heat which produces a change of state to give us an indication of the temperature. In the same way we could use any of the effects of heat. The blacksmith makes a lot of use of the colour effect. When he is tempering his tools he does not use any particular instrument to tell him when to plunge the tool into the water or the oil. He heats the tool until it glows a certain colour and he knows that the temperature has then reached the required value for successful tempering. Turning tools and chisels are normally tempered by heating them at the cutting end until the metal glows cherry-red and then quenching them in oil.

The most accurate method of measuring temperature is by making use of either the first or the last of the above effects of heat. The Thermometer is an instrument for measuring temperatures by means of expansion of either liquids or metals. The Pyrometer indicates temperature readings by means of the small electrical current produced when heat is applied to the thermocouple.

The Thermometer

This consists of a glass tube having a very fine uniform bore. This is called a capillary tube. One end of the tube is sealed and formed into a bulb. A liquid, usually mercury, is inserted into the tube, the air is forced out and the other end of the tube sealed. The two most common liquids used in thermometers are mercury and alcohol. The choice depends upon the type of work which the thermometer has to do. For example, alcohol boils at a temperature lower than that of water. Alcohol would therefore be quite unsuitable for thermometers required to measure temperatures as high as boiling water. Again, the mean temperature at the North Pole in January is considerably lower than the freezing point of mercury. Hence, if a mercury thermometer were taken to the North Pole at this time of the year the mercury would freeze solid and the thermometer would be no use for temperature measurements. Both these difficulties are overcome if a mercury thermometer is used for temperatures normally encountered in this country, and an alcohol thermometer is used on Arctic expeditions. Due to alcohol being a colourless liquid it is necessary to add some colouring, usually red, so that the level of the liquid in the tube can be read easily.

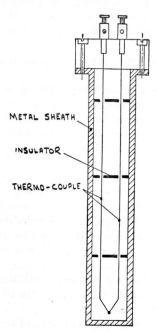

METAL SHEATH

INSULATOR

THERMO-COUPLE

FIG. 77—THE PYROMETER
An instrument for measuring high temperatures by electrical means.

The Pyrometer

The pyrometer is an instrument which measures the temperature of a body by measuring the small electrical current produced when heat is applied to a thermocouple. Fig. 77 shows a sectional arrangement of one type of pyrometer. Two wires of dissimilar metals are welded together at one end and joined to separate terminals at the other ends. They are insulated from each other by means of mica washers and in some cases by passing through narrow bore porcelain tubes.

Various pairs of metals are used depending upon the temperature range required. Copper and constantan, nickel and nickel-chrome, are two pairs frequently used. The delicate wires are mounted in a steel sheath for protective pur-

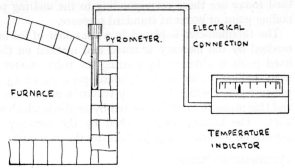

FIG. 78—Diagram showing the arrangement of the pyrometer and connections for measuring the temperature of a furnace.

poses. Specially designed connecting wires connect the pyrometer with an electrical galvanometer which measures the quantity of electrical current flowing in the circuit. The readings on the galvanometer dial are direct in degrees of temperature.

Fig. 78 shows how the pyrometer is used in measuring the temperature of an electrical furnace. The instrument is mounted in the side of the furnace to avoid reducing the available space of the furnace. The galvanometer can be mounted on an adjoining wall or it may be placed in a control office together with other instruments to allow for a central control of the heat treatment operations. A special recording gear is often used in conjunction with the pyrometer so that the variation of the temperature from hour to hour throughout the day can be shown graphically in a similar manner to that of barometer recordings often seen in opticians' windows.

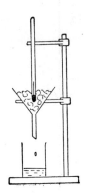
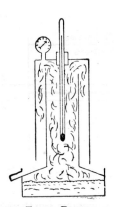

FIG. 79—DETERMINATION OF THE FIXED POINTS
OF A THERMOMETER
O° C. or 32° F. is obtained by surrounding the thermometer with ice. 100° C. or 212° F. is obtained by standing the thermometer in steam from boiling water at atmospheric pressure.

Fixed Points

Before marking the scale on a thermometer it is necessary to determine the position of the two " fixed points." The " fixed points " used today are those corresponding to the melting point of ice and the boiling point of water at standard pressure.

The thermometer is placed in a container of ice and the lowest level reached by the mercury is noted and marked on the tube. The other fixed point is obtained by putting the thermometer in steam produced from boiling water at a standard pressure of 15 lb. per sq. in. A pressure gauge will indicate any variation in pressure from the standard, and this pressure can be corrected by methods which will become familiar later. The highest level reached by the mercury is then noted and marked on the tube. Fig. 79 indicates the method used in these two cases.

Thermometer Scales

There are two types of scales in common use today : the **Fahrenheit** and the **Centigrade**. On the Fahrenheit scale, named after the man who suggested its use, the boiling point of water is marked as 212° and the melting point of ice is marked as 32°. There are therefore 180 divisions between the two points. In the case of the Centigrade scale the corresponding figures are 100° for boiling point of water and 0° for the melting point of ice. There are 100 divisions or gradations in this scale. The name Centigrade means 100 divisions.

The Fahrenheit scale is used mainly in medical and meteorological work while the Centigrade scale which is used extensively in physics is replacing the Fahrenheit scale in engineering. Care must be taken in carrying out any calculation to see that the facts given all relate to the same temperature scale.

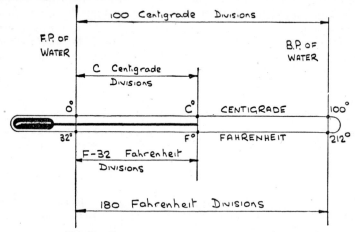

FIG. 80—FAHRENHEIT AND CENTIGRADE SCALES

100 Centigrade divisions are equal to 180 Fahrenheit divisions. The relationship between Centigrade and Fahrenheit temperatures is given by the formula :

$$\frac{C}{5} = \frac{F-32}{9}.$$

Temperature Conversion

It is often necessary to convert a temperature reading from one scale to another. A simple conversion formula is used based on the following reasons.

In two identical thermometers the distance between the two fixed points is the same. If one thermometer is to be marked with a Centigrade scale and the other with a Fahrenheit scale, then the Centigrade thermometer will have 100 divisions between the two marks and the Fahrenheit one will have 180 divisions. The Fahrenheit divisions will appear smaller than the Centigrade divisions. In fact:

180 *Fahrenheit divisions will be equal to* 100 *Centigrade divisions,*

or 1 Fahrenheit division $= \dfrac{100}{180} = \dfrac{5}{9}$ Centigrade division

and 1 Centigrade division $= \dfrac{180}{100} = \dfrac{9}{5}$ Fahrenheit divisions.

In addition to this difference of size of division, we must also take into account the fact that the Fahrenheit scale begins at 32° while the Centigrade scale begins at 0°. Suppose both thermometers are placed in the same liquid and the Centigrade thermometer reads C.° and the figure on the Fahrenheit thermometer is F.°. The temperature is therefore

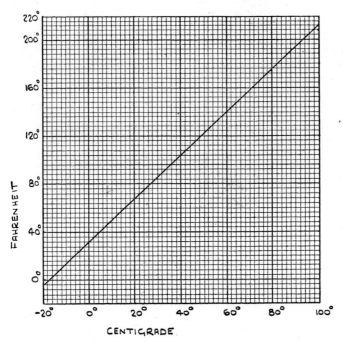

Fig. 81—Temperature Conversion Graph

C centigrade divisions above the melting point of ice, i.e., $C \times \frac{9}{5}$ Fahrenheit divisions above the melting point of ice, which is marked as $32°$.

The Fahrenheit reading F will be $(C \times \frac{9}{5}) + 32$, and we have the following equation :

$$\left(C \times \frac{9}{5}\right) + 32 = F$$

$$C \times \frac{9}{5} = F - 32$$

$$\frac{C}{5} = \frac{F - 32}{9}$$

Fig. 81 gives a conversion chart from which the corresponding temperatures can quickly be obtained.

The following examples illustrate the use which can be made of the conversion formula.

Example 49.—(1) Convert (a) $10°$ C. into $°$ F., and (b) $131°$ F into $°$ C.

(a) $\dfrac{C}{5} = \dfrac{F - 32}{9}$

Substitute 10 for C

$$\frac{10}{5} = \frac{F - 32}{9}$$

$$2 \times 9 = F - 32$$

$$18 + 32 = F$$

$$F = 50$$

∴ $10°$ C. $= 50°$ F. **Ans.**

(b) $\dfrac{C}{5} = \dfrac{F - 32}{9}$

Substitute 131 for F

$$\frac{C}{5} = \frac{131 - 32}{9}$$

$$= \frac{99}{9}$$

$$\therefore \frac{C}{5} = 11$$

$$C = 55$$

∴ $131°$ F. $= 55°$ **C. Ans.**

Example 50.—Convert (a) $- 15°$ C. into $°$ F., and (b) $- 300°$ F. into $°$ C.

(a) $\dfrac{C}{5} = \dfrac{F - 32}{9}$

Substitute $- 15$ for C

$$\frac{- 15}{5} = \frac{F - 32}{9}$$

$$- 3 \times 9 = F - 32$$

$$32 - 27 = F$$

$$F = 5°$$

∴ $- 15°$ C. $= + 5°$ F. **Ans.**

(b) $\dfrac{C}{5} = \dfrac{F - 32}{9}$

Substitute $- 300$ for F

$$\frac{C}{5} = \frac{- 300 - 32}{9}$$

$$= \frac{- 332}{9}$$

$$\therefore C = \frac{- 332 \times 5}{9}$$

$$= \frac{- 1660}{9}$$

$$= - 184\frac{4}{9}$$

∴ $-300°$ F. $= -184\frac{4}{9}°$ C. Ans

Example 51.—The temperatures of the liquids in two baths are recorded as 55° C. and 180° F. What would the thermometers read if they were interchanged?   N.C.T.E.C.

$$\frac{C}{5} = \frac{F - 32}{9} \qquad\qquad \frac{C}{5} = \frac{F - 32}{9}$$

Substitute 55 for C   Substitute 180 for F

$$\frac{55}{5} = \frac{F - 32}{9} \qquad\qquad \frac{C}{5} = \frac{180 - 32}{9}$$

$$11 \times 9 = F - 32 \qquad\qquad = \frac{148}{9}$$

$$99 + 32 = F \qquad\qquad C = \frac{740}{9}$$

$$F = 131° \text{ Ans.} \qquad\qquad = 82\tfrac{2}{9}° \text{ Ans.}$$

When the thermometers are interchanged they will read 131° F. and $82\tfrac{2}{9}$° C.

EXERCISE 7

(1) Change 56° C. to ° F., and change 56° F. to ° C.

(2) Centigrade and Fahrenheit thermometers placed in two different hot liquids read 65° C. and 113° F. respectively. What will they read when interchanged?

(3) An accurate Centigrade thermometer reads 35° when placed in a certain liquid. A Fahrenheit thermometer placed with it reads 94·8°. Determine the amount of error in the Fahrenheit thermometer.

(4) Rewrite the following statement using the Fahrenheit scale: "The heater only raises the temperature of water 25° C. so that, in winter, when the temperature of the tap water is usually below 10° C. a really hot bath cannot be obtained by means of it."

(5) A Centigrade thermometer, when placed into a beaker of water, reads 16° C. What should be the reading of a Fahrenheit thermometer placed into the same water?

(6) An accurate Centigrade thermometer reads 40° when placed in a certain liquid. A Fahrenheit thermometer placed in the same liquid reads 103·7°. Determine the amount of error in the Fahrenheit thermometer.

(7) The following important temperatures are given in ° C. What are the corresponding Fahrenheit temperatures:

(a) Bunsen burner flame   ..   ..   ..   1600° C.
(b) Sun ..   ..   6000° C.
(c) Normal temperature of human body ..   37° C.
(d) Boiling point of mercury   ..   ..   357° C.
(e) Freezing point of mercury   ..   ..   −38·9° C.
(f) Boiling point of alcohol   ..   ..   78° C.

(g) Freezing point of alcohol .. .. −114° C.

(h) Mean temperature at North Pole in
    January .. .. −41° C.

(8) (a) Convert the following temperatures to the Fahrenheit scale:
10° C., 70° C., 2° C.

(b) Find the temperature at which the Centigrade and Fahrenheit
scales record the same reading.   N.C.T.E.C.

CHAPTER 9

QUANTITY OF HEAT

There are two types of problems which lead us to a study of quantity of heat. Suppose that we have a large tank full of water at room temperature, say 15° C., and that we want to raise its temperature to 80° C. We must have some means of determining the amount of heat that we shall require to do this. It will be obvious that the amount of heat required will depend upon the amount of liquid and upon the numbers of degrees of temperature rise. It may not be as obvious that the quantity of heat is also dependent upon the nature of the liquid. We shall find, for example, that we need much more heat to raise the temperature of a quantity of water than we should to raise the temperature of the same quantity of sulphuric acid through the same number of degrees. In fact we should require three times as much heat for the water than for the acid ; and that means that we should require three times as much fuel and that the cost would be three times as great.

This leads to the second type of problem. The main fuels which we use for heating purposes are coal, gas, and some liquid fuels such as petrol and paraffin. In the case of heating by electricity, the fuel is burned at the power house and the heat energy is converted into electrical energy which can be reconverted to heat when required. The question is : If we know how much heat we require for any heating operation, how can we determine how much fuel we shall need and hence the fuel cost of the operation. Or, alternatively, if we have a sample of each of two types of coal of equal weight, can we obtain any idea of the quantity of heat which each sample will " give out," or liberate, when completely burned. Because this will be an important consideration when choosing a type of coal to be used in any boiler plant.

The units in which quantities of heat are measured are *based upon the heat required to raise, by one degree, a unit amount of water.* The name and value of the unit depends upon the quantity of water and the scale in which we measure the temperature rise. These are the units usually employed.

The **Calorie** is the amount of heat required to raise the temperature of one **gram** of water by one degree **Centigrade.**

The **Centigrade Heat Unit (C.H.U.)** is the amount of heat required to raise the temperature of one **pound** of water by one degree **Centigrade.**

The **British Thermal Unit (B.Th.U.)** is the amount of heat required to raise the temperature of one **pound** of water by one degree **Fahrenheit.**

There is also a larger unit used particularly in connection with gas engineering called the Therm. **One Therm = 100,000 B.Th.U.s**

The calorie, which is not often used in engineering, is sometimes called the gram-calorie to distinguish it from the Centigrade Heat Unit sometimes called the pound-calorie.

Unit	Quantity of Water	Temperature Scale
Calorie	One gram	Centigrade
Centigrade Heat Unit (C.H.U.)	One pound	Centigrade
British Thermal Heat Unit (B.Th.U.)	One pound	Fahrenheit

Since 1 Centigrade degree is $\frac{9}{5}$ times as large as the Fahrenheit degree, we shall expect to find that more heat is required to raise the temperature of 1 lb. of water by one degree Centigrade than by one degree Fahrenheit; in other words, the Centigrade Heat Unit will be larger than the British Thermal Unit. The relationship between the two is:

1 Centigrade Heat Unit $= \frac{9}{5}$ British Thermal Units

1 British Thermal Unit $= \frac{5}{9}$ Centigrade Heat Units.

Calorific Value of Fuel

The calorific value of a fuel is the number of heat units released when a unit amount of the fuel is burned. For example, the calorific value of Diesel oil is 18,000 B.Th.U. per lb. This means that 18,000 B.Th.U. are released when 1 lb. of the oil is burned. The calorific value of some of the more important fuels is given in the following table. We shall see at a later stage that it is usual to quote two different figures in connection with the calorific value of most fuels, but at this stage we shall deal with only the one figure whose meaning will be taken as given above.

TABLE 3

Fuel	Calorific Value (C.H.U.)
Anthracite coal ..	8500 per lb.
Bituminous coal ..	8000 per lb.
Coke	7200 per lb.
Dry wood	4500 per lb.
Hydrogen	34,500 per lb.
Petrol	11,000 per lb.
Diesel oil	10,000 per lb.
Town gas	280 per cub. ft.

In order to get a true comparison with the figure for the town gas it may be noted that 1 lb. of this gas occupies 31 cub. ft., and therefore the calorific value may be expressed as 31 × 280 = 8680 C.H.U. per lb. Each gas-producing authority is now required by law to state the calorific value of its gas. You will find the value quoted on a copy of the gas bill. On the bill to which I am referring are the words : " To gas supplied at the declared calorific value of 500 B.Th.U.s per cub. ft." The reason for this ruling will be clear when you remember that your gas meter registers the flow of gas in cub. ft. The registration is independent of the quality of gas. It would still register the same if air were passing through the meter. Therefore in order to ensure that the customer is obtaining full heat value for his money the producer must guarantee that every cub. ft. of gas passing through the meter will contain a stated quantity of heat units.

Efficiency of Heating Plant

No heating or boiler plant is perfect. In no case is the whole of the heat supplied by the fuel used entirely in heating the water. Some of the heat is used in heating the containing vessel, some passes up the chimney, some is transferred through the containing vessel to the air outside. Only a part of the heat supplied is usefully employed in heating the water. The efficiency of the plant gives an idea of the ratio of the heat supplied to the heat usefully employed.

$$\text{Efficiency \%} = \frac{\text{heat used in heating water}}{\text{total heat supplied}} \times 100.$$

If we transpose this formula we can obtain one which will tell us how much heat must be supplied in order to allow for the inefficiency of the boiler plant.

The transposition will be :

$$\text{Heat to be supplied} = \frac{\text{heat used in heating water}}{\text{efficiency (\%)}} \times 100.$$

Example 52.—How much heat will be required to raise the temperature of 300 lb. of water from 15° C. to 70° C. ?

Temperature rise = 70−15 = 55 Centigrade degrees
Quantity of water = 300 lb.
Heat required = 300 × 55
= 16,500 Centigrade Heat Units. **Ans.**

Example 53.—Find the cost of raising the temperature of 5000 gall. of water from 20° C. to 80° C. using coal whose calorific value is 8000 C.H.U. per lb. and whose cost is £2 per ton. The boiler plant is 75% efficient.

$$\text{Temperature rise} \qquad = 80 - 20 = 60 \text{ Centigrade degrees}$$
$$\text{Quantity of water} \qquad = 5000 \text{ gall.}$$
$$= 5000 \times 10 \text{ lb. (1 gall. water}$$
$$\text{weighs 10 lb.)}$$
$$= 50,000 \text{ lb.}$$
$$\text{Heat required} \qquad = 50,000 \times 60 \text{ C.H.U.s.}$$
$$\text{Heat to be supplied} \qquad = \frac{50,000 \times 60 \times 100}{75}$$
$$= 4,000,000 \text{ C.H.U.s.}$$
$$\text{1 lb. of coal contains} \qquad 8000 \text{ C.H.U.s}$$
$$\therefore \text{ weight of coal required} = \frac{4,000,000}{8000} \text{ lb.}$$
$$= 500 \text{ lb.}$$
$$\text{Cost of coal at £2 per ton} = \frac{500}{2240} \times 2 \times 20 \text{ shillings}$$
$$= 8 \cdot 93 \text{ shillings}$$
$$= 8\text{s. } 11\tfrac{1}{2}\text{d. } \textbf{Ans.}$$

Specific Heat

We must now extend the principles, which so far have been applied to the heating of water, so that we can determine the quantity of heat required to raise the temperature of any substance. By experiment it can be shown that in the case of equal weights of water and copper at the same temperature the water contains much more heat than the copper. If we take a 1 lb. block of copper at a temperature of 97° C. and place it in 1 lb. of water at 20° C., the resulting temperature of the water would be approximately 27° C. If we take 1 lb. of water at 97° C. and pour it into another 1 lb. of water at 20° C. the resultant temperature would be approximately 58° C. The cold water in the second case has been able to extract more heat from the hot water than was extracted from the copper in the first case. This is shown by the fact that the final temperature of the cold water is higher in the second case than in the first.

In a similar manner we could compare the heat which could be extracted from any substance with that which could be extracted from the same weight of water at the same temperature. Water is taken as the basis of comparison. The heat required to raise the temperature of a given weight of a substance has been found experimentally and compared with the amount of heat required to raise the temperature of the same weight of water by the same amount. This comparison or ratio is expressed as a numerical value known as the **Specific Heat.**

$$\frac{\textbf{Specific heat}}{\textbf{of substance}} = \frac{\textbf{heat required to raise temp. of 1 lb. of substance 1°.}}{\textbf{heat required to raise temp. of 1 lb. of water 1°.}}$$

Note—The temperatures may be Fahrenheit or Centigrade but the same units must be used for the substance as for the water.

When we say that the *specific heat of copper is* 0·1 *we mean that a given weight of copper requires* 0·1 *times the amount of heat to raise its temperature that the same amount of water requires for the same temperature rise.* The figure can be interpreted another way when we remember that 1 lb. of water requires 1 C.H.U. to raise its temperature 1° C. One lb. of copper therefore requires 0·1 × 1 or 0·1 C.H.U. to raise its temperature 1° C. The specific heat of a substance therefore is numerically equal to the number of C.H.U.s (or B.Th.U.s) required to raise the temperature of 1 lb. of the substance 1° C. (or 1° F.).

The expressions for determining heat quantities can now be given in their general form.

Heat required = quantity of substance × specific heat × temp. rise.

Heat given out $\Big\}$ *= quantity of substance × specific heat × temp. drop.*
in cooling

The table below gives the specific heat of the more common substances.

TABLE 4

TABLE OF SPECIFIC HEATS

Water	..	..	1·0	Tin..	..	..	0·056
Ice ..	..	..	0·5	Copper	..	..	0·1
Alcohol	..	..	0·65	Iron	..	..	0·11
Turpentine	..	..	0·47	Aluminium	..	..	0·21
Mercury	..	..	0·033	Lead	..	..	0·031

Example 54.—How much heat is required to raise the temperature of 10 lb. of iron from 20° C. to its melting point 1280° C. ?

Heat required = quantity × sp. ht. × temp. rise
  = 10 × 0·11 × (1280 − 20)
  = 1·1 × 1260
  = **1386 C.H.U.s since temperatures are given in**
    Centigrade scale. Ans.

Example 55.—How much heat is given out when the temperature of 8 lb. of copper falls from 540° F. to 140° F. ? If all the heat given out could be transferred to 10 lb. of water at a temperature of 108° F., what would be the final temperature of the water ?

Heat given out = quantity × sp. ht. × temp. drop
  = 8 × 0·1 × (540 − 140)
  = 0·8 × 400
  = **320 B.Th.U.s since temperatures are given in**
    Fahrenheit scale. Ans.

Let the final temperature of the water be $t°$ F.

Temperature rise $=$ (final $-$ original) temperatures

$$= (t - 108).$$

Heat supplied $=$ quantity $\times$ sp. ht. $\times$ temp. rise.

$$320 = 10 \times 1 \times (t - 108)$$
$$= 10(t - 108).$$
$$32 = t - 108.$$
$$32 + 108 = t.$$

Final temperature of the water is 140° F. Ans.

Mixtures and Transference of Heat

Fig. 82 shows diagrammatically the arrangement of an experiment which could be carried out to give the results used in Example 55.

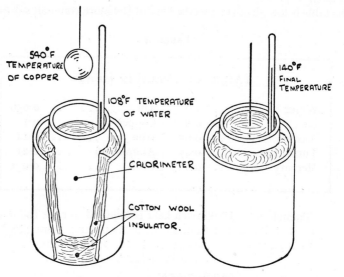

FIG. 82—DETERMINATION OF SPECIFIC HEAT OF COPPER

The initial temperature and the weight of the copper is known. It is then immersed into a known weight of water whose temperature has been recorded. If the final temperature of the copper and the water is noted, the specific heat of the copper can be found by equating the heat lost by the copper to the heat gained by the water.

An 8 lb. copper ball, approximately $3\frac{5}{8}$ in. diameter, is heated to a temperature of 540° F. and then placed into 10 lb. of water at 108° F. The temperature of the water rises, and the temperature of the copper falls until they both reach the same value, 140° F. If the two substances are in contact then their temperatures must ultimately become the same. During the process of adjusting temperatures the copper loses heat and the water gains heat.

The heat lost by the copper is equal to the heat gained by the water. This is a very important principle and questions dealing with the transference of heat in mixtures make use of this principle. The relationship as stated is only true if the following assumptions are made.

(1) That no heat is lost to any external body. This will be nearly true if we take care to prevent any splashing and if the vessel containing the water is surrounded with cotton wool. The vessel containing the water and the thermometer will both absorb some heat since their temperature will always be the same as that of the water. The vessel is usually made of copper and is called a **calorimeter.** We shall see how we can make allowance for the heat absorbed by the calorimeter.

(2) That none of the water is converted into steam. Since the copper is at a much higher temperature than that at which water normally boils, it is quite possible that steam will be formed. This can be reduced to a minimum if the copper is plunged into the water quickly.

There are a variety of problems dealing with heat transference, the following being a selection of the more usual.

Example 56.—Two lb. of water at 100° C. are mixed with 3 lb. of water at 20° C. Find the final temperature of the mixture.

Let t° C. equal final temperature of mixture.

$$\text{Heat lost by hot water} = \text{quantity} \times \text{sp. ht.} \times \text{temp. drop}$$
$$= 2 \times 1 \times (100 - t) \text{ C.H.U.s}$$
$$\text{Heat gained by cold water} = \text{quantity} \times \text{sp. ht.} \times \text{temp. rise}$$
$$= 3 \times 1 \times (t - 20) \text{ C.H.U.}$$
$$\text{Heat gained} = \text{heat lost}$$
$$3(t - 20) = 2(100 - t)$$
$$3t - 60 = 200 - 2t$$
$$5t = 260$$
$$t = 52°.$$

Final temperature of the mixture is 52° C. Ans.

Example 57.—A ball of copper weighing 200 grams is placed in a flue until its temperature is equal to that of the flue gases. It is lowered into 580 c.c.s of water at 15° C. and the resulting temperature of the water is observed to be 30° C. What is the temperature of the flue gases ?

Let t° C. equal temperature of flue gases.

Note that in this example weights are given in grams and since the temperatures are in the Centigrade scale the heat quantities are calories. Also since 1 c.c. of water weighs 1 gram. the quantity of water is 580 grams.

Heat lost by copper   = quantity × sp. ht. × temp. drop
     = 200 × 0·1 × $(t - 30)$ calories
     = 20 $(t - 30)$ calories.
Heat gained by water   = quantity × sp. ht. × temp. rise
     = 580 × 1 × $(30 - 15)$ calories
     = 580 × 15 calories.
Heat lost = heat gained.
$$20 (t - 30) = 580 × 15$$
$$t - 30 = \frac{580 × 15}{20}$$
$$t - 30 = 435$$
$$t = 465.$$

Temperature of flue gases is 465° C.

Example 58.—In order to determine the specific heat of aluminium 30 grams of the metal was placed in water at 100° C. until it attained the temperature of the water. It was then transferred to 150 grams of water at a temperature of 20° C. The final temperature of the cold water was 25° C. Determine the specific heat of the aluminium.

Let s equal specific heat of aluminium.

Heat lost by aluminium = quantity × sp. ht. × temp. drop
     = 30 × s × $(100 - 25)$
     = 30 × 75s calories.
Heat gained by water = quantity × sp. ht. × temp. rise
     = 150 × 1 × $(25 - 20)$
     = 150 × 5 calories.
Heat lost = heat gained.
$$30 × 75s = 150 × 5$$
$$s = \frac{150 × 5}{30 × 75}$$
$$= 0·33.$$

Specific heat of aluminium = 0·33. Ans.

Example 59.—In an experiment to determine the specific heat of iron the following results were obtained :

Weight of iron	200 grams
Initial temperature of iron	98° C.
Weight of water	150 grams
Weight of copper calorimeter	100 grams
Specific heat of copper	0·1
Initial temperature of water	18° C.
Final temperature of water	28° C.

Calculate the specific heat of the iron.

Let s equal specific heat of iron.

Heat lost by iron   = quantity × sp. ht. × temp. drop

                      = 200 × s × (98 − 28)

                      = 200 × 70s calories.

Heat gained by water   = quantity × sp. ht. × temp. rise

                      = 150 × 1 × (28 − 18)

                      = 150 × 10 calories.

Heat gained by calorimeter = quantity × sp. ht. × temp. rise

                      = 100 × 0·1 × (28 − 18)

                      = 10 × 10 calories.

Total heat gained   = (150 × 10) + (10 × 10)

                      = (150 + 10) × 10

                      = 160 × 10

                      = 1600 calories.

$$\text{Heat lost} = \text{heat gained.}$$
$$200 \times 70s = 1600$$
$$s = \frac{1600}{200 \times 70}$$
$$= 0{\cdot}114.$$

Specific heat of iron = 0·114. Ans.

Example 60.—A copper calorimeter of weight 12·5 grams contains 50 grams of a liquid at 10° C. Into the liquid is placed 100 grams of copper at 100° C. and the temperature rises to 38·5° C. Find the specific heat of the liquid, assuming the specific heat of copper to be 0·1.   N.C.T.E.C.

Let s equal specific heat of liquid.

Heat lost by copper   = quantity × sp. ht. × temp. drop

                      = 100 × 0·1 × (100 − 38·5)

                      = 615 calories (weight given in grams).

Heat gained by liquid   = quantity × sp. ht. × temp. rise

                      = 50 × s × (38·5 − 10)

                      = 1425s calories.

Heat gained by calorimeter = quantity × sp. ht. × temp. rise

                      = 12·5 × 0·1 × (38·5 − 10)

                      = 35·625 calories.

$$\text{Heat gained} = \text{heat lost.}$$
$$1425s + 35{\cdot}625 = 615$$
$$1425s = 579{\cdot}375$$
$$s = \frac{579{\cdot}375}{1425}$$
$$= 0{\cdot}37$$

The specific heat of the liquid is 0·37. Ans.

EXERCISE 8

(1) If the specific heat of steel is 0·110, what would be the rise of temperature of a gallon of water at 40° F. if 10 lb. of steel balls, at 200° F., were suddenly thrown in ? (1 gall. of water weighs 10 lb.)

(2) A piece of iron weighing 2 lb. heated to cherry red heat was dropped into an iron pail weighing 3 lb. and containing 15 lb. of water. The rise in temperature of the water and pail was 15° C. Determine the fall in temperature of the hot iron if the specific heat of iron is 0·1.

(3) A piece of copper weighing 200 grams is heated to 100° C. and placed in 100 grams of alcohol at 8° C., contained in a copper calorimeter of weight 25 grams. The temperature is observed to rise to 28·5° C. If the specific heat of copper is 0·095 find that of alcohol.

(4) A copper ball of weight 500 grams is placed in a furnace and left until it has attained the furnace temperature. It is then placed in a copper calorimeter weighing 200 grams and containing 1980 grams of water at 15° C. If the temperature of the water rises to 35° C., what is the temperature of the furnace ? (Specific heat of copper = 0·1.)

(5) In an experiment to determine the specific heat of a certain kind of oil, 54 grams of boiling water were added to 58·4 grams of oil in a container weighing 65 grams and of specific heat 0·1. If the temperature of the cold oil was 15° C. and that of the mixture 75° C., find the specific heat of the oil.

(6) An aluminium calorimeter weighs 28·10 grams empty, and 80·70 when some water at 15·2° C. has been poured into it. An aluminium cylinder weighing 79·60 grams is raised to 98·8° C. and dropped into the calorimeter, raising the temperature of the water to 34·0° C.

(a) Find the specific heat of aluminium.

(b) Find the water equivalent of the calorimeter.

(7) If 100 grams of water at 100° C. are poured into 120 grams of turpentine at 9° C. and the resulting temperature found to be 70° C., what is the specific heat of turpentine ?

(8) The specific heat of lead is 0·031.

200 grams of lead are heated up to 100° C. and dropped into a calorimeter containing 100 grams of a liquid whose specific heat is 0·6 and whose temperature is 12° C. Calculate the final temperature of the liquid if the calorimeter absorbs no heat.

(9) The specific heat of copper is 0·1.

100 grams of water at 100° C. are poured into 120 grams of turpentine at 9° C. The turpentine is in a copper calorimeter weighing 40 grams. If the resulting temperature is 65° C., what is the specific heat of turpentine ?

(10) With gas costing 1s. 4d. per therm, how much would it cost to fill a 20-gall. bath by means of a geyser if the geyser raised the water temperature from 58° F. to 108° F., assuming that 10% of the heat supplied is wasted   (1 gall. of water weighs 10 lb.)

(11) In a hot water heating system, 2000 lb. of water circulate per hour. At the boiler the temperature of flow is 180° F., and the temperature of return 140° F.   If the calorific value of coal is 13,000 B.Th.U. per lb. and its cost is £4 per ton, find the cost of maintaining the circulation per 12-hour day.

(12) What is the cost of heating 5000 gall. of water from 20° C. to 100° C. by means of a 75% efficient boiler plant, using coal whose calorific value is 8500 C.H.U. per lb. and whose cost is £3 per ton.

(13) Calculate the number of units of heat required to raise the temperature of 200 grams of oil from 16° C. to 60° C. if the specific heat of the oil is 0·4. If this amount of heat is supplied to 50 grams of water at 10° C. contained in a copper vessel of weight 30 grams, find the temperature attained by the water if the specific heat of copper is 0·1.

(14) A gas geyser, using gas of 450 B.Th.U. per cub. ft. calorific value, supplies 100 gall. of water at 185° F. per day, the inlet temperature being 60° F. The gas costs 10d. per therm. As much heat as is usefully employed is lost in the waste gases. Find how many therms are used in a quarter of 13 weeks. What is the cost of using the geyser in this period ? What volume of gas has been used in the period ?

(15) In a test to determine the calorific value of a sample of coal, 0·0015 lb. of coal were burned in heating 2 lb. of water, contained in a calorimeter of water equivalent 0·2 lb., from 14° C. to 19·6° C.
Assuming that there was no loss of heat, find :
  (a) The quantity of heat given up by the coal.
  (b) The calorific value of the coal in C.H.U. per lb.

(16) The calorific value of petrol is 19,000 B.Th.U. per lb. and that of coal gas is 250 C.H.U. per lb. Convert these figures to C.H.U. and B.Th.U. respectively.

(17) In a test on a gas engine 360 lb. of water are circulated per hour. The water enters the engine at 15° C. and leaves it at 50° C. Calculate the heat carried away per minute in C.H.U. and B.Th.U.

(18) In a test with a coal calorimeter 0·002 lb. of coal were burned and heated 2 lb. of water from 15° C. to 21·5 C. How much heat does the water receive ? Allowing 10% for radiation losses find :
  (a) Total heat given out by the coal.
  (b) Calorific value of the coal in C.H.U. per lb.

(19) Define the Centigrade Heat Unit and the British Thermal Unit. 20 lb. of a liquid having a specific heat 0·6 is at a temperature 15° C. when mixed with 25 lb. of water at 50° C. Assuming no external loss of heat, find the temperature reached by the mixture. Describe briefly the precautions taken to avoid loss of heat during the experiment.
N.C.T.E.C.

(20) Make a neat sketch showing the relationship between the Fahrenheit and Centigrade scales of temperature.

A piece of steel weighing 4 lb. and at a temperature of 300° C. was immersed in 4 gall. of water in a small tank. To measure the temperature of the water there was only a Fahrenheit thermometer available. If the initial temperature of the water was 60° F., what was the probable maximum temperature of the water in degrees Fahrenheit? Ignore all heat losses. (Specific heat of steel is 0·117; 1 gall. of water weighs 10 lb.)   N.C.T.E.C.

(21) A piece of copper of weight 8 oz. and at a temperature of 100° C. is dropped into 10 oz. of a liquid at 16° C. If the temperature of the liquid rises to 30° C. find its specific heat. (Specific heat of copper = 0·09.)   N.C.T.E.C.

(22) The exhaust gases from an oil engine are passed through a water heater. The gases have a specific heat of 0·25 and the temperature falls from 420° C. to 150° in flowing through the heater, the flow being 50 lb. per min. If the water enters the heater at 40° C. and flows at the rate of 80 lb. per min. find its temperature at exit.   N.C.T.E.C.

(23) When 30 C.H.U. are given to a piece of metal weighing 15 lb. the temperature rises from 12° C. to 18·3° C. Find the specific heat of the metal.   N.C.T.E.C.

(24) What is meant by " specific heat "?

A piece of steel weighing ¾ lb. is heated in a hardening furnace to 800° C. and quenched by plunging into an oil bath containing 7·5 lb. of oil at a temperature of 30° C. If the specific heat of the steel is 0·117 and the final temperature of the oil and steel is 50° C., determine the specific heat of the oil. Neglect the weight and material of the bath and ignore any heat losses.   N.C.T.E.C.

CHAPTER 10

LATENT HEAT

We have seen that when heat is applied to water the temperature of the water increases. This increase of temperature continues until a temperature is reached, known as the **SATURATION TEMPERATURE** at which the water begins to boil. Although heat is continually supplied to the water there is no further increase in temperature. There is, however, a change in state produced from water to steam, and we must conclude that the additional heat supplied is used in producing this change. To distinguish between the work done by the two supplies of heat we use the terms " **sensible heat** " and " **latent heat.**"

Sensible heat is the heat which produces an **increase in the temperature** of the substance to which it is applied. A substance is assumed to have no sensible heat at 0° C. and 32° F. If 40 C.H.U.s are supplied to 1 lb. of water at 0° C. its temperature will increase to 40° C. The sensible heat in the water will then be 40 C.H.U. at 40° C.

In general, sensible heat in water at $T°$ $C = T$ C.H.U. per lb.

If 40 B.Th.U.s are supplied to 1 lb. of water at 32° F. its temperature will increase to 72° F. The sensible heat in the water will then be 40 B.Th.U. at 72° F.

In general, sensible heat in water at $T°$ F. $= (T - 32)$ B.Th.U. per lb.

Latent heat is the heat which produces a **change of state** without a change of temperature. The word latent means " hidden." Now since there are two changes of state possible with a substance, viz., from solid to liquid and from liquid to vapour, there are also two forms of latent heat producing the respective changes.

" **Latent heat of fusion** " is the heat required to change unit quantity of solid to liquid at the same temperature.

" **Latent heat of vaporisation** " is the heat required to change unit quantity of liquid to vapour at the same temperature.

The value of the latent heat of a substance depends upon the pressure at which the change takes place. Since we are concerned chiefly with water, the following figures are important and should be memorised. At normal pressures of 15 lb. per sq. in. the latent heat of fusion of ice is 80 C.H.U. per lb. or 144 B.Th.U. per lb. The latent heat of vaporisation of water (usually referred to simply as the latent heat of steam) is 540 C.H.U. per lb. or 970 B.Th.U. per lb. These figures mean, for example, that 1 lb. of water at 100° C. requires 540 C.H.U. to change it into 1 lb. of steam at the same temperature 100° C. when the pressure is 15 lb. per sq. in.

The total heat of 1 lb. of steam is the sum of the sensible heat and the latent heat.

Total heat = sensible heat + latent heat.

The following tables give the saturation temperature, the sensible and the latent heat of steam for various pressures.

TABLE 5

Centigrade Units

Pressure lb. per in.²	Saturation Temperature ° C.	Sensible Heat C.H.U. per lb.	Latent Heat C.H.U. per lb.
15	100	100	540
20	109	109	534
25	116	116	530
30	121	122	526
50	138	139	515
100	164	166	496
150	181	184	483
200	194	197	472
300	214	219	455

Fahrenheit Units

Pressure lb. per in.²	Saturation Temperature ° F.	Sensible Heat B.Th.U. per lb.	Latent Heat B.Th.U. per lb.
15	212	180	970
20	228	196	961
25	240	208	953
30	250	219	947
50	281	250	926
100	328	298	892
150	358	331	868
200	382	355	848
300	417	394	815

Boiler Efficiency

In large-scale production of steam, various types of modern boilers are used. These boilers are designed to try to make use of all the heat which is liberated when the fuel is burned. Some of this heat, however, does escape ; some passes through the flues and up the chimney, some is lost in radiation (you can feel the radiated heat as you stand in front of the boiler), some is carried away by the continuous stream of red hot ashes. This means that only a fraction of the heat available in the fuel is transferred to the water in the boiler to convert it into steam.

Total heat of 1 lb. of steam = sensible heat + latent heat (both values from the tables).

Sensible heat in 1 lb. of feed water at $t°$ C. = t C.H.U.

Sensible heat in 1 lb. of feed water at $t°$ F. = $(t - 32)$ B.Th.U.

Heat required to produce 1 lb. of steam = total heat of steam − sensible heat of feed water.

If W lb. of steam are produced per lb. of fuel burned :

$$\text{Boiler efficiency} = \frac{\text{heat required to produce W lb. of steam}}{\text{heat contained in 1 lb. of fuel}}$$

Note on Pressures

When a boiler pressure gauge indicates 80 lb. per sq. in. the pressure is given as 80 lb. per sq. in. above the pressure of the atmosphere which may be taken as 15 lb. per sq. in. Hence the actual pressure or the **absolute pressure** of the steam is 80 + 15 = 95 lb. per sq. in. The first pressure (80 lb. per sq. in.) is termed the **gauge pressure.**

Absolute pressure = gauge pressure + atmospheric pressure.

Example 61.—How much heat is required to convert 5 lb. of ice at − 20° C. into steam at 100° C. ? The pressure is 15 lb. per sq. in. and the specific heat of ice is 0·5.

Heat to raise temp. of 5 lb.
of ice from −20° C. to 0° C. = quantity × sp. ht. × temp. rise
= 5 × 0·5 × (0 − (− 20))
= 5 × 0·5 × 20
= 50 C.H.U.

Heat to convert 5 lb. of ice
at 0° C. into 5 lb. of water
at 0° C. = quantity × latent heat
= 5 × 80
= 400 C.H.U.

Heat to raise temp. of 5 lb.
of water from 0° C. to
100° C. = quantity × sp. ht. × temp. rise
= 5 × 1 × (100 − 0)
= 500 C.H.U.

Heat to convert 5 lb. of
water at 100° C. into 5 lb.
of steam at 100° C.   = quantity × latent heat
                         = 5 × 540
                         = 2700 C.H.U.
Total heat required = 50 + 400 + 500 + 2700
                         = **3650 C.H.U. Ans.**

Example 62.—A rectangular reservoir 150 ft. long and 80 ft. wide contains water 10 ft. deep which is to be raised in temperature from 2° C. to 14° C. by blowing in steam at 100° C. Calculate the weight of steam required.

Volume of reservoir   = 150 × 80 × 10
                         = 120,000 cub. ft.
Weight of water   = 120,000 × 62·5 lb. (1 cub. ft.
                             weighs 62·5 lb.)
                         = 7,500,000 lb.
Required temperature rise   = 14 − 2
                         = 12° C.
Total heat required   = 7,500,000 × 12 C.H.U.
Let W lb. equal weight of steam required.
Final temperature of steam   = 14° C.
Heat given up by 1 lb. of
steam at 100° C. cooling
down to 14° C.   = [540] + [1 × 1 × (100 − 14)]
                         (latent heat) + (sensible heat)
                         = 626 C.H.U.
Heat given up by W lb. of
steam   = 626W C.H.U.
           626 W   = 7,500,000 × 12
$$W = \frac{7,500,000 \times 12}{626}$$
                         = 143,770 lb.
Amount of steam required   = **143,770 lb. Ans.**

Example 63.—If heat at a rate of 500 C.H.U. per min. is applied to 400 lb. of water contained in an open vessel at a temperature of 15° C., find the time that will elapse before 20 lb. of the water is converted into steam.

Heat required to raise temp. of 400 lb. of water from 15° C.
         to 100° C. = quantity × sp. ht. × temp. rise
                     = 400 × 1 × (100 − 15)
                     = 34,000 C.H.U.

Heat required to convert 20 lb. of the water at 100° C. into
steam at 100° C. = quantity × latent heat

$$= 20 \times 540$$
$$= 10,800 \text{ C.H.U.}$$

Total heat required $\quad = 34,000 + 10,800$
$$= 44,800 \text{ C.H.U.}$$

Heat is supplied at 500 C.H.U. per min.

$$\therefore \text{ time taken} = \frac{44,800}{500} = 89\cdot6 \text{ min.} \quad \textbf{Ans.}$$

89·6 min. will elapse before 20 lb. of the water is converted
into steam.

Example 64.—Taking the latent heat of ice as 80 C.H.U. per
lb. find the resulting temperature produced by placing 4 lb. of
ice at 0° C. into 20 lb. of water at 25° C.

Let $t°$ C. be the final temperature.

Heat lost by water = 20 × 1 × $(25 - t)$ C.H.U.

Heat gained by ice = latent heat + sensible heat

$$= (4 \times 80) + [4 \times 1 \times (t - 0)]$$
$$= 320 + 4t$$

Heat lost = heat gained

$$20(25 - t) = 320 + 4t$$
$$500 - 20t = 320 + 4t$$
$$180 = 24t$$
$$t = \frac{180}{24}$$
$$= 7\tfrac{1}{2}°$$

Final temp. of mixture is $7\tfrac{1}{2}°$ C. **Ans.**

Example 65.—A boiler produces dry steam at a pressure of
200 lb. per sq. in. from feed water at 40° C. 9·6 lb. of steam are
generated per lb. of coal burnt. The calorific value of the coal is
8000 C.H.U. per lb. What is the thermal efficiency of the boiler ?

Sensible heat of steam at 200 lb. per sq. in. = 197 C.H.U. per lb.

Latent heat of steam at 200 lb. per sq. in. = 472 C.H.U. per lb.

Total heat in 1 lb. of steam $\quad\quad\quad = 669$ C.H.U.

Sensible heat in feed water at 40° C. $\quad = 40$ C.H.U. per lb.

∴ heat required to convert 1 lb. of feed water into 1 lb. of steam

$$= 669 - 40$$
$$= 629 \text{ C.H.U.}$$

Heat used in producing 9·6 lb. steam $\quad = 9\cdot6 \times 629$ C.H.U.

Heat in 1 lb. of coal $\quad\quad\quad\quad\quad\quad = 8000$ C.H.U.

Thermal efficiency $= \dfrac{\text{heat to convert feed water into steam}}{\text{heat supplied by coal}}$

$$= \frac{9\cdot6 \times 629}{8000} = 0\cdot75 \text{ or } 75\%. \quad \textbf{Ans.}$$

Example 66.—An oil fired boiler generates steam at 212° F. from feed water at 55° F., the efficiency being 75%. Calculate the weight of steam generated per lb. of oil burned taking the calorific value of oil as 18,000 B.Th.U. per lb.

Let W lb. of steam be generated per lb. of oil burned.

Total heat of 1 lb. of steam at 212° F.

$$= \text{sensible heat} + \text{latent heat}$$
$$= 180 + 970$$
$$= 1150 \text{ B.Th.U.}$$

Sensible heat in 1 lb. of feed water at 55° F. $= 55 - 32$
$$= 23 \text{ B.Th.U.}$$

∴ heat required to produce 1 lb. of steam $= 1150 - 23$
$$= 1127 \text{ B.Th.U.}$$

Heat required to produce W lb. of steam $= 1127\text{W B.Th.U.}$

$$\text{Heat supplied by oil} = \frac{\text{heat to produce steam}}{\text{efficiency}}$$

$$= \frac{1127\text{W}}{0 \cdot 75} \text{ B.Th.U.}$$

This can be equated to 18,000 B.Th.U., the calorific value of 1 lb. of oil producing W lb. of steam.

$$\therefore \frac{1127\text{W}}{0 \cdot 75} = 18,000$$

$$\text{W} = \frac{0 \cdot 75 \times 18,000}{1127}$$

$$= 11 \cdot 9 \text{ lb.}$$

1 lb. of oil generates 11·9 lb. of steam. Ans.

EXERCISE 9

(1) Three grams of steam at 100° C. are passed into 50 grams of water at 20° C. What will be the resulting temperature of the water?

(2) If the specific heat of ice is 0·5, how much heat is necessary to convert 5000 grams of ice at −10° C. into steam at 100° C.? The latent heat of vaporisation of water is 540 calories per gram, and the latent heat of fusion of ice is 80 calories per gram.

(3) Find the latent heat of steam at 100° C. from the following test results:

Weight of calorimeter	105 grams
Weight of calorimeter and water	346 grams
Initial temperature of calorimeter and water ..	4° C.
Final temperature of calorimeter and water ..	24° C.
Weight of calorimeter and contents after experiment	354·16 grams
Temperature of steam	99·7° C.
Specific heat of copper calorimeter	0·1

(4) A rectangular reservoir 200 ft. long and 100 ft. wide contains water to a depth of 15 ft. which is to be raised in temperature from 4° C. to 20° C. by blowing in steam at 100° C. Calculate the weight of steam required.

(5) A boiler produces dry steam at a pressure of 200 lb. per sq. in. from feed water at 40° C. ; 9 lb. of steam are generated per lb. of coal burned. The calorific value of the coal is 7600 C.H.U. per lb. What is the efficiency of the boiler ?

(6) A boiler whose efficiency is 80% raises 2600 lb. of dry steam per hour at a pressure of 300 lb. per sq. in. from feed water at 60° C. The coal has a calorific value of 7500 C.H.U. per lb. How many lb. of coal are required per hour ?

(7) A boiler generates steam at atmospheric pressure from feed water at 23° C. The calorific value of the coal used is 8100 C.H.U. per lb. and the boiler efficiency is 70%. What weight of coal is needed per hour when evaporating 9000 lb. of water per hour ?

(8) An oil fired boiler generates steam at 100° C. from feed water at 12° C. the efficiency being 80%. Calculate the weight of steam generated per lb. of oil burned, taking the calorific value of coal as 10,500 C.H.U. per lb.

(9) A gas fired boiler generates dry steam at 212° F. at a rate of 110 lb. per hour from feed water at 60° F. The calorific value of the gas is 450 B.Th.U. per cub. ft. and 30% of this heat is wasted. Calculate the gas consumption per hour.

(10) Explain the meaning of sensible heat and total heat of dry saturated steam. Determine the number of heat units required to generate 3000 lb. of dry saturated steam at an absolute pressure of 200 lb. per sq. in. from water at 80° C.

Abs. Press.	Temp. C.	Sensible Heat C.H.U.	Total Heat
200	194·4	197·5	669·7

U.L.C.I.

(11) Twelve gall. of water at 15° C. are mixed in an open tank with 20 gall. of water at 90° C. Neglecting any heat losses, determine the resulting temperature of the mixture formed.

If the whole of the mixture is now heated in the tank to 100° C. and one half of the water contents of the tank is then evaporated into steam, calculate how many C.H.U. will be required to carry out this combined process, if all heat losses are neglected. You are given that the latent heat of steam at atmospheric pressure is 539 C.H.U. per lb. and that 1 gall. of water weighs 10 lb.   N.C.T.E.C.

(12) What is meant by (a) latent heat, (b) sensible heat ?

A tank containing 10 gall. of water had dry steam blown into it. The initial temperature of the water in the tank was 16° C. The latent heat of steam supplied was 534 C.H.U. per lb. and its sensible heat above 0° C. was 109 C.H.U. per lb. The final temperature of the mixture was 60° C. Neglecting the effect of the tank, determine the weight of steam that was blown into the tank. One gallon of water weighs 10 lb.

N.C.T.E.C.

(13) Explain the meaning of the terms "sensible heat," "latent heat," and "total heat" as applied to the generation of steam. Find the number of heat units required to generate 2000 lb. of dry saturated steam from water at 60° C. if the sensible heat of the steam is 184 C.H.U. per lb. and the total heat 666 C.H.U. per lb. Show sensible heat and latent heat separately.   N.C.T.E.C.

(14) If heat at the rate of 200 C.H.U. per min. is applied to 200 lb. of water contained in an open vessel at a temperature of 15° C., find the time that will elapse before 20 lb. of the water is converted into steam. Latent heat of steam 540 C.H.U. per lb.   N.C.T.E.C.

(15) Explain clearly the terms "sensible heat" and "latent heat." A boiler supplies steam at a pressure of 100 lb. per sq. in. from water at 60° F. At this pressure the latent heat per lb. of steam is 890 B.Th.U. per lb. and the boiling temperature 328° F. What heat will be required to be supplied to evaporate 1 lb. of the water into steam at this pressure ?

The fuel used 15,000 B.Th.U. per lb. If 65% of this heat is usefully employed in forming the steam, how many lb. of steam will be formed per lb. of fuel ?   N.C.T.E.C.

(16) A kettle holding 1 quart of water at 12° C. is placed over a lighted gas ring. How much heat is required to raise the temperature of the water to boiling point ? How much heat is wasted if the gas is left on until half the water is boiled away ? Neglect heat not transferred to the water. What weight of the water would this wasted heat have raised to the boiling point ? The latent heat of water at atmospheric pressure may be taken as 538 C.H.U. per lb. and the weight of a gallon of water as 10 lb.   N.C.T.E.C.

CHAPTER II

EXPANSION OF SOLIDS

We have seen that the mercury thermometer depends for its action upon the increase in the length of a mercury column which takes place when heat is applied to the mercury. This change in length, or expansion, takes place when heat is applied to most substances to a greater or lesser degree. The amount of increase depends upon three factors.

(1) *The Original Size of the Substance.* We should expect to find that the expansion in a continuous length of 1 mile of railway line would be much greater than in a 3-in. long nail, other conditions being equal.

(2) *The Temperature Rise.* We have noticed that the change in length of the mercury column is much greater for a 100° temperature rise than for a 10° temperature rise.

(3) *The Substance Itself.* It is found that a 10-in. column of mercury will expand by 0·182 in. for a temperature rise of 100° C., while the same length of steel will expand 0·0118 in. for the same temperature rise, i.e., only one fifteenth of the amount.

You may be thinking that in the case of a thermometer a much greater expansion is noticed than that quoted above. The reason for the apparently large expansion is due to the relatively large volume of mercury in the bulb. The expanding

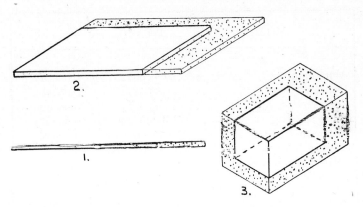

FIG. 83—THREE TYPES OF EXPANSION
(1) Linear expansion. When the breadth and depth are small in relation to the length. E.g., railway lines.
(2) Superficial expansion or expansion of area. The thickness is small compared with the length and breadth. E.g., a zinc roof covering.
(3) Cubical expansion or expansion of volume. E.g., the expansion of a solid block of metal.

143

M.E.S. I—5*

mercury is forced into a very narrow bore tube and therefore occupies a long length of tube.

Coefficient of Expansion

The amount by which a unit length of a substance will expand when the temperature is increased from 0° C. to 1° C. (or 32° F. to 33° F.) has been determined experimentally and is known as the **coefficient of expansion** of the substance. In practice we shall find that for any temperature rise of one degree we shall take the coefficient of expansion to mean the increase in unit length for any temperature rise of one degree.

If we are dealing with the expansion of a railway line we are concerned with the increase in the **LENGTH** of the line and we shall require to know the " **coefficient of linear expansion** " of the metal.

If we are dealing with the expansion of a sheet of zinc roofing we shall be concerned not only with the increase of length but also the increase of breadth, in other words with the increase of **AREA**. In this case we shall require to know the " **coefficient of superficial expansion** " of the metal.

If we are dealing with the expansion of a block of metal then we shall find that all three dimensions change and that we can determine the increase in **VOLUME** if we are told the " **coefficient of cubical expansion.**"

For the present we shall only be concerned with change in length particularly applied to metals and shall use the coefficient of linear expansion or more simply the coefficient of expansion.

TABLE 6
Coefficient of Expansion

Metal	Per 1° C.	Per 1° F.
Aluminium	0·000022	0·000012
Iron and Steel	0·000011	0·000006
Copper	0·000017	0·000010
Brass	0·000019	0·000011
Platinum	0·000008	0·000004
" Invar "	0·0000001	0·00000005
(Iron alloy with 36% nickel)		

Take the case of copper. The above figure means that :

1 in. of copper expands by 0·000017 in. for 1° C. rise, or

1 ft. of copper expands by 0·000017 ft. for 1° C. rise, or

1 metre of copper expands by 0·000017 metres for 1° C. rise,

and so on.

If the temperature rise were measured in degrees Fahrenheit then the corresponding figure would be 0·000010.

If we had a 2° C. rise in temperature we should get double the expansion, i.e., 0·000034 in.   If we had 3 in. of copper we should find that the expansion would be three times as much, i.e. :

$$0·000017 \times 3 \qquad = 0·000051 \text{ in. for } 1° \text{ C. rise, and}$$
$$0·000017 \times 2 \times 3 = 0·000153 \text{ in. for } 2° \text{ C. rise.}$$

This leads to the formula for calculating expansion amounts.

Expansion = original length × coefficient of expansion × temp. rise
New length = original length + expansion.

Let L_0 = original length at temp. t_0

L = new length at temp. t

a = coefficient of expansion

d = amount of expansion

$$d = L_0 \times a \times (t - t_0)$$
$$L = L_0 + d$$
$$= L_0 + L_0 a(t - t_0)$$
$$= L_0 [(1 + a(t - t_0)]$$

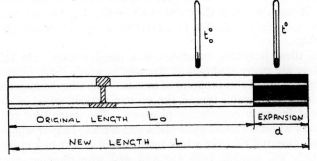

FIG. 84—THE EXPANSION OF A RAILWAY LINE
The amount of expansion d depends upon :
    (1) The original length of the rail L_0
    (2) The temperature rise $(t - t_0)$
    (3) The material.
New length = original length + expansion.

Expansion and contraction of metals proves to be a mixed blessing to the engineer.   Allowance must be made for changes in length, particularly where (*a*) there is a long length of metal, or (*b*) very high temperatures are anticipated.

In the first class we have the most common example of railway lines which have to be laid with a gap between the sections.   This gap is the cause of the characteristic railway noise which railway engineers are seeking to eliminate.   Steam and hot water pipes are usually mounted on rollers and are so arranged to allow expansion to take place along the length of the room.   If this is impracticable, an expansion joint is inserted in the length of the pipe. Special arrangements have to be provided in steel or iron bridges. Recently the Sydney Harbour bridge (span approximately $\frac{1}{3}$ mile) expanded by $9\frac{1}{2}$ in. during the afternoon of a very hot day. The Firth of Forth bridge, the total length of the water spans being just over 1 mile, is 8 ft. 6 in. longer on a warm summer's day than on a cold winter's day. If these structures were not free to expand, their members would be subjected to very high stresses and would in all probability fail by buckling. It may be noted that no gaps are left between the sections of rails which are laid in the ground, such as tram-rails. These are, in fact, welded together. Since these rails are well bedded in concrete and the various other road materials there is no fear of buckling taking place. Any temperature rise will, therefore, produce compressive stresses in the rails. In any case, the variation in temperature will be less noticeable with rails laid in the ground than with rails mounted on sleepers.

In the second case we have the various moving parts of heat engines —pistons, slide valves, and turbine rotors—all of which have to be reasonably tight fitting to prevent pressure losses while at the same time being capable of motion. If the piston and the cylinder are made of the same material they will have the same expansion for the same temperature rise. Any variation in expansion is usually taken up by the piston rings.

In all these instances expansion is a disadvantage. On the other hand there are many examples of the way in which the engineer makes very effective use of this property of metals. The time-honoured method of tightly fixing a metal tyre or rim on to a wooden wheel by shrinking is adopted in many engineering processes. The outer tyre and flange of a railway wheel is shrunk on to the wheel centre. In gear wheel design, it is often essential that the wheel teeth should be cut in a special alloy steel which will provide both strength and wear-resisting properties. The cost of making the whole wheel in this alloy would be excessive. Hence the wheel centre is usually a steel casting and the alloy steel rim, which may be 5 to 6 ft. diameter, 12 to 24 in. wide, 1 to 2 in. thick, depending upon the design, is heated with gas jets until it will just slip over the machined centre. On cooling down, the grip which it exerts on the centre is sufficient to transmit the power between the teeth and the wheel shaft without any additional means of securing the rim. In some small components the reverse process is often adopted. The centre is placed in a refrigerator and cooled down so that the diameter contracts so that the centre can be dropped into the outer member.

Change of length following change of temperature suggests a convenient method of controlling the temperature variation of a room, by a thermo-stat or of giving warning of excessive increase of temperature. A bi-metal strip (a strip of brass riveted to a strip of steel), originally straight will bend into an arc with the steel on the inside as the tem-

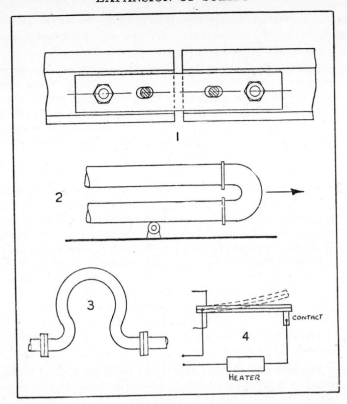

FIG. 85—EXPANSION OF METALS

(1) A gap has to be left between railway lines to allow for expansion. A slot is also provided in the two fish plates to allow movement to take place.

(2) Circulating pipes mounted on rollers. The top pipe returns underneath to allow the pipes to expand in the direction of the arrow. The pipes are not built in at this end.

(3) Expansion joint. In some cases it is not practicable to make arrangements as in 2. A circular expansion joint will allow the necessary movement of the pipes to take place.

(4) The compound bar (steel at the top, brass underneath) originally straight will bend as shown dotted as the temperature rises. It can thus be arranged to break an electrical contact to switch off an electric heater. The temperature of the room can thus be controlled.

perature increases. This is due to the difference in the coefficient of expansion of the metals. The brass strip will expand more than the steel strip. The bent strip can be made either to make or break electrical contact, and thus either give warning of the temperature rise, or cut out an electrical supply of heat. This supply will be switched on again as the temperature falls causing the bar to straighten and re-make the contact. One design of gas-control valve works with an expanding rod

moving across the gas supply pipe thus reducing the supply and consequently lowering the temperature.   By this means the temperature of
an oven can be maintained at a predetermined value.

Example 67.—A length of steel piping is 100 ft. long at 20° C.
Find the increase in length when steam at 220° C. passes through
it. Coefficient of expansion for steel = 0·000012 per ° C.

Increase in length = original length × coefficient of expansion
$$\times \text{ temp. rise}$$
$$= 100 \times 0.000012 \times (220 - 20) \text{ ft.}$$
$$= 100 \times 12 \times 0.000012 \times 200 \text{ in.}$$
$$= 2.88 \text{ in.   Ans.}$$

Example 68.—An aluminium piston is turned to a diameter of
5 in., the temperature being 70° during the process. When in use
in a cylinder the temperature of the piston is 400° F. What increase
in diameter of the piston in thousandths of an inch, will have taken
place ? Coefficient of expansion of aluminium is 0·000012 per ° F.

Increase in diameter = original diameter × coefficient of
$$\text{expansion} \times \text{temp. rise}$$
$$= 5 \times 0.000012 \times (400 - 70) \text{ in.}$$
$$= 5 \times 0.000012 \times 330$$
$$= 0.0198 \text{ in.   Ans.}$$

The diameter of the piston will increase 19·8 thousandths of an
inch or 19·8 " thous."

Example 69.—A steel tyre is to be fitted over a locomotive
wheel, 2 metres in diameter, to fit tightly when the tyre is 100° C.
above the temperature of the wheel.   The coefficient of linear
expansion of steel is 0·000011 per ° C. To what internal diameter
must the tyre be turned ? In order to allow the tyre to be positioned it must be expanded to 2·008 metres. Through what total
range of temperature must it be raised ?

(*a*) In the limiting condition for tightness, the diameter of
the tyre must be equal to the diameter of the wheel
when the temperature of the tyre is 100° C. above that
of the wheel.

Consider the tyre when its diameter is 2 metres ; let
its temperature drop by 100° C., i.e., let it cool down to
room temperature.

Contraction = original diameter × coefficient of expansion
$$\times \text{ temp. drop}$$
$$= 2 \times 0.000011 \times 100 \text{ metres}$$
$$= 0.0022 \text{ metres } (0.22 \text{ cm.})$$

∴ Internal diameter of tyre at room temperature:
$$= 2 - 0.0022$$
$$= 1.9978 \text{ metres.   Ans.}$$

Internal diameter of tyre must be turned to 1·9978 metres.

(b) For positioning, the internal diameter must be 2·008 metres.

Let $t°$ C. = temp. rise required above that at which internal diameter is 2 metres.

Required expansion is 0·008 metres.

Expansion = original diameter × coefficient of expansion
$$\times \text{ temp. rise}$$

$$0·008 = 2 \times 0·000011 \times t$$
$$t = \frac{0·008}{2 \times 0·000011}$$
$$= 364° \text{ C.}$$

Tyre must be heated through a total temperature range of 100 + 364 = 464° C. Ans.

EXERCISE 10

(1) A copper rod is 2 metres long at 0° C. How many millimetres will it increase in length when heated to 160° C. ? The coefficient of expansion of copper is 0·000017.

(2) A platinum wire is 0·1335 cm. longer at 70° C. than at 20° C. If the coefficient of linear expansion of platinum is 0·000089, what is the length of the wire at 20° C. ? Determine the length of the wire at 100° C.

(3) A copper rod 50 cm. long is heated from 15° C. to 95° C. If the coefficient of expansion of copper is 0·000017 find the amount which the rod will expand.

(4) A copper wire is 60 yds. long in winter. How much longer will it be in summer if the change in temperature is 45° C. ? (The coefficient of linear expansion of copper is 0·000017 per ° C.)

(5) The switch in an electrically-operated thermostat for controlling the temperature of a hot-water supply tank is worked by the expansion of a copper rod 14 in. long at 18° C. If the switch is to operate at 85° C., find the expansion of the rod necessary to work the switch. Coefficient of linear expansion of copper = 0·000017 per ° C.

(6) If the coefficient of linear expansion in iron is 0·000011 per ° C., calculate the allowance in inches which must be made for expansion in each of the four tubes of the Britannia bridge over the Menai Straits if each tube has a minimum length of 460 ft. and the range of temperature is 60° C.

(7) An endless cable used in an aerial railway is 4000 ft. long at 32° F. What will be the increase in length of the cable when the temperature rises to 72° F. ? Coefficient of expansion = 0·000012 per ° C.

(8) An aluminium piston is turned to a diameter of 4 in., the temperature being 65° F. during the process. When in use in a cylinder, the

temperature of the piston is 425° F. What increase in diameter of the piston, in thousandths of an inch, will have taken place? The coefficient of linear expansion of aluminium is 0·000012 per ° F.

(9) An iron tyre is bored out to a diameter of 42 in. at 40° F. and is to be fitted to a wooden wheel. The tyre is heated to 640° F. and is then fitted on to the wheel. Find the greatest diameter to which the wheel may be constructed if there must be a margin of 0·02 in. to allow the tyre to be positioned on the wheel. (Coefficient of linear expansion of iron is 0·000007 per ° F.)

(10) A steel tyre is to be slipped over a locomotive wheel, 6 ft. in diameter, to fit tightly when the tyre is 100° C. over the temperature of the wheel. The coefficient of linear expansion of steel is 0·000011 per ° C. To what internal diameter must the tyre be turned? To allow the tyre to be positioned it must be expanded to 72·2 in. Through what total range of temperature must it be raised?

(11) An aluminium piston is turned to a diameter of 6 in., the temperature being 70° F. during the process. When in use in a cylinder the temperature of the piston is 450° F. What increase in diameter of the piston will have taken place? The coefficient of linear expansion of aluminium is 0·000012 per ° F.

(12) Describe any experiment concerned with the expansion of a metal due to rise of temperature.

A bar 4 ft. long has its temperature increased from 50° C. to 450° C. Find the increase in length in inches. Coefficient of linear expansion, 0·00002 per ° C.   N.C.T.E.C.

(13) A steam pipe 20 ft. long at 15° C. carries steam at a temperature of 250° C. What will be the length under steaming conditions? Briefly, how would this increase in length be allowed for in practice?

(Take the coefficient of linear expansion as 0·0000108 per ° C.)
    N.C.T.E.C.

(14) In an experiment a metal rod 40 in. long, firmly fixed at one end and free at the other, is heated through 84° C. By means of a micrometer placed at the free end the expansion was found to be 0·056 in. Calculate the coefficient of linear expansion of the metal.   N.C.T.E.C.

(15) What is meant by " the coefficient of linear expansion of a metal "?

A steel crank arm is to be shrunk on to the crankshaft. The hole in the crank arm is 9·99 in. diameter at 15° C. and is required to be 10·04 in. diameter when heated. To what temperature must the arm be heated for this diameter to be obtained? The coefficient of linear expansion of steel is 0·000012 per ° C.   N.C.T.E.C.

(16) A copper pipe in a heating system is 30 ft. long at the normal temperature of 15° C.; find its length when water at a temperature of 85° C. flows through it. Coefficient of expansion of copper per ° C. ⇌ 0·000017.   U.L.C.I.

CHAPTER 12

MECHANICAL EQUIVALENT OF HEAT

We shall have noticed that whenever any machining is being done the tool quickly becomes hot. In fact in many operations a quantity of coolant is poured over the tool and workpiece to keep the temperature reasonably low, so that the operation can be efficiently carried out. There are many examples of heat being produced when movement takes place between two materials. A shaft rotating in a bearing can produce sufficient heat, if not sufficiently lubricated, to cause it to expand and bind itself in the bearing or cause " seizure." Even if this extreme does not occur we shall find that a bearing becomes appreciably warmer after the shaft has been running some time. In a worm gear drive the threads of the steel worm are continually sliding over the tooth surface on the bronze wheel and a considerable amount of heat is produced. It is part of the duty of the designer to make sure that the heat generated is reduced to a minimum and that which is generated is removed as quickly as possible. During the flight of pilotless rockets, their speeds become so high that passage through the atmosphere is a relatively difficult matter. So much heat is generated, due to friction between the skin of the rocket and the atmosphere, that the temperature rises to 600° C. and the projectile would be visible at night. For the same reason projectiles moving through the universe often pass through the atmosphere surrounding the earth. In their case they become white hot and are often seen moving across the sky and are given the name " shooting stars." As they pass out of the atmosphere they cool down and become invisible to the naked eye.

Now the immediate question is, where does heat come from and how is it produced? In all cases we shall find that the heat produced is dependent upon two factors :

(1) The speed of movement between the two surfaces in contact, e.g., drill and workpiece ; shaft and bearing ; worm and wheel ; rocket and air.

(2) The resistance which one surface offers to the movement of the other surface.

The association of movement with resistance brings us back to the idea of work done. The work which the shaft has to do in overcoming friction in the bearing is converted into heat. The work which the rockets do in overcoming the frictional resistance of the air is converted into heat. What is the relationship between the amount of work done and the quantity of heat produced ?

Count Rumford, engaged on boring out cannon at the German Naval
Arsenal, noticed that the metal removed by the boring tool was very
hot. He arranged to carry out the boring operation under water using a
very blunt tool. The heat produced was sufficient to boil the water in a
very short time.

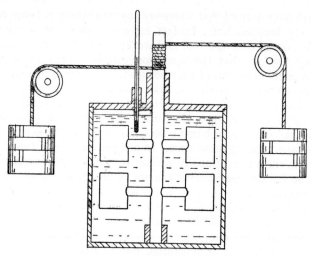

FIG. 86—DETERMINATION OF MECHANICAL EQUIVALENT OF HEAT
The falling weights drive the paddles in the water.   Due to the resistance
of the water heat is generated and the temperature of the water rises.
If the weight of the water is known together with the water equivalent
of the calorimeter and the temperature rise it is possible to calculate
the amount of heat produced by the falling weights.

In 1843 Joule performed experiments in Manchester to determine the
relationship between the heat generated and the work done. The apparatus which he used is shown diagrammatically in Fig. 86.   A paddle wheel
immersed in water was rotated by weights. The weights were allowed to
fall through a known distance, wound back to their initial position and
then allowed to fall again. This was repeated a number of times. An
arrangement was provided to allow the weights to be lifted without
turning the paddles back. The amount of work done by the falling
weights was found by multiplying the magnitude of the weights by the
total distance through which they fell. The rise in temperature of the
water was noted and the amount of heat produced by the paddles was
calculated by multiplying the temperature rise by the mass of the water.
Allowance was made for heat absorbed by the calorimeter and corrections
were also applied to take into account radiation losses. Joule found
that 772 ft. lb. of work was equivalent to 1 B.Th.U. Further experiments
have shown that a more accurate figure is:

778 ft. lb. of work is equivalent to 1 B.Th.U.

or 1400 ,,   ,,   ,,   ,, 1 C.H.U.

These figures are known as Joule's Mechanical Equivalent of Heat and are usually denoted by J.

Although not laying within the province of this book, it will be useful to mention here the relationship between electrical and mechanical units of power and hence to connect them both with heat units.

The Watt is the basic unit of electrical power.

The Kilowatt is equal to 1000 watts.

Now 1 **horsepower is equal to 746 watts,**

i.e., 550 ft. lb. per sec. is equal to 746 watts.

1 ft. lb. per sec. is equal to 1·36 watts.

778 ft. lb. per sec. is equal to 1055·4 watts,

i.e., 1 B.Th.U. per sec. is equal to 1055·4 watts or 1·055 kilowatts.

This means that a 1-kilowatt electric kettle will produce approximately 1 B.Th.U. per sec.

Example 70.—A 1-kilowatt kettle holds 2 pints of water. How long will it take to boil the water assuming that the temperature of the cold water is 52° F.?

$$\text{Temperature rise} = 212 - 52$$
$$= 160° \text{ F.}$$

$$\text{Mass of water} = \frac{2}{8} \times 10 \quad (1 \text{ gall.} = 8 \text{ pints} = 10 \text{ lb.})$$

$$= 2\tfrac{1}{2} \text{ lb.}$$

$$\text{Heat required} = 2\tfrac{1}{2} \times 160 \text{ B.Th.U.}$$
$$= 400 \text{ B.Th.U.}$$

1 kilowatt is approximately 1 B.Th.U. per sec.

∴ **the kettle will take 400 sec. to provide 400 B.Th.U.,**

i.e., **6 min. 40 sec. Ans.**

Due to radiation losses the kettle will require a slightly longer time.

Example 71.—An electrical generator has an output of 5 kilowatts. If 1 h.p. = 746 watts, calculate the output of the generator in horsepower. This output is 22% of the heat supplied by the fuel used by the engine which drives the generator. How much fuel having a heating value of 10,000 C.H.U. per lb. is consumed per hour?   N.C.T.E.C.

5 kilowatts = 5000 watts.

$$= \frac{5000}{746} \text{ h.p.}$$

$$= 6·7 \text{ h.p.}$$

Let W lb. of fuel be supplied per hour.

Then heat units supplied per hour = 10,000 W C.H.U.

Output of generator $= \dfrac{22}{100} \times 10,000$ W

$\qquad = 2200$ W C.H.U. per hour

$\qquad = 2200 \times 1400$ W ft. lb. per hour

$\qquad = \dfrac{2200 \times 1400 \text{ W}}{60}$ ft. lb. per min.

$\qquad = \dfrac{2200 \times 1400 \text{ W}}{60 \times 33,000}$ h.p.

But output is 6·7 h.p.

$\therefore \quad \dfrac{2200 \times 1400 \text{ W}}{60 \times 33,000} = 6\cdot7$

$\qquad\qquad \text{W} = \dfrac{60 \times 33,000 \times 6\cdot7}{2200 \times 1400}$

$\qquad\qquad\quad = 4\cdot31$ lb.

Fuel consumption per hour $= 4\cdot31$ lb.   Ans.

Example 72.—The combustion of 1 lb. of fuel oil generates 12,000 C.H.U. If 65% of the heat is wasted, find how long a 250 h.p. oil engine, working at full load, would take to consume 300 lb. of fuel.

Let t hours be the time to consume 300 lb. fuel.

Heat supplied $= 300 \times 12,000$ C.H.U.

Since 65% is wasted 35% must be useful heat.

$\therefore$ Heat converted to work $= 300 \times 12,000 \times 0.35$ C.H.U.

Heat converted to work per min. $= \dfrac{300 \times 12,000 \times 0\cdot35}{60\,t}$ C.H.U.

Since 1 C.H.U. $= 1400$ ft. lb. the work done per min. is :

$$\dfrac{300 \times 12,000 \times 0\cdot35 \times 1400}{60t} \text{ ft. lb.}$$

$\therefore$ H.P. $= \dfrac{300 \times 12,000 \times 0\cdot35 \times 1400}{60t \times 33,000}$

Equating this to 250 we get :

$$250 = \dfrac{300 \times 12,000 \times 0\cdot35 \times 1400}{60t \times 33,000}$$

$$t = \dfrac{300 \times 12,000 \times 0\cdot35 \times 1400}{250 \times 60 \times 33,000}$$

$$= 3\cdot55 \text{ hours.   Ans.}$$

EXERCISE 11

(1) An oil engine develops 20 h.p. and has a thermal efficiency of 30%. It uses oil having a calorific value of 10,500 C.H.U. per lb. How long will the engine run on 1 lb. of oil ?

(2) How long should a 4 h.p. motor cycle run on 1 gall. of petrol if 0·2 of the energy of the fuel is converted into useful work? Calorific value of petrol is 120,000 C.H.U. per gall.

(3) In a modern power station the electrical output, per boiler, is 20,000 kilowatts. 20,000 lb. of coal are supplied per hour to the boiler. The calorific value of the coal is 11,500 B.Th.U. per lb. Determine: (a) Heat supplied in B.Th.U. per min. (b) Output of the station in B.Th.U. per min. (c) Thermal efficiency of the plant.

(4) What is the horsepower of an engine which uses 30 lb. of oil per hour, calorific value 20,000 B.Th.U. per lb., if 25% of the heat supplied is converted into useful work?

(5) An engine converts 30% of the heat supplied into useful work. If the calorific value of the fuel is 18,000 B.Th.U. per lb., calculate the horsepower of the engine per lb. of fuel supplied. The engine uses 3 lb. of fuel per hour.

(6) Determine the petrol consumption of an engine which has a thermal efficiency of 25% when it is developing 12 h.p. The calorific value of the petrol is 100,000 C.H.U. per gall.

(7) An electrical generator has a rated output of 8 kilowatts. Calculate the output of the generator in horsepower. If this output represents 24% of the heat supplied by the fuel whose calorific value is 12,000 C.H.U. per lb., how much fuel is consumed per hour?

(8) A 2-kilowatt immersion heater is used to heat a supply of water. The water is supplied at 20° C. Determine the time taken to raise the temperature of 10 gall. of water to 85° C.

(9) A tank contains 750 gall. of a liquid, specific heat 0·6, density 0·8 (i.e., 1 gall. of the liquid weighs 8 lb.). Boiling point 90° C. If the initial temperature of the liquid is 15° C., determine the time required to boil the liquid using four 2-kilowatt heaters. If the electrical energy is supplied at a cost of one halfpenny per unit (i.e., 1 kilowatt-hour), what will be the cost of the operation?

(10) An oil engine is used to drive an electric generator. The oil used has a heat value of 18,000 B.Th.U. per lb. and the engine transforms 25% of this heat into useful work which it employs in driving the generator. The generator in turn transforms 80% of the energy it receives into electrical energy.

If the engine uses 5 lb. of this fuel per hour, what will be: (a) The horsepower of the engine (b) The electrical output of the generator? (Take 1 B.Th.U. = 778 ft. lb. ; 1 h.p. = 746 watts.)   N.C.T.E.C.

(11) Find the mechanical energy in ft. tons equivalent to the heat energy required to convert 10 cwt. of water at 15° C. into steam at atmospheric pressure. Latent heat of steam, 540 C.H.U. per lb.
                                                                    N.C.T.E.C.

(12) The bearing friction in a machine absorbs 2·5 h.p. If all of this power is converted into heat, calculate the C.H.U. per hour. N.C.T.E.C.

(13) Explain what is meant by the " mechanical equivalent of heat."
The combustion of 1 lb. of fuel oil generates 10,120 C.H.U. If 70%
of the heat is wasted, find how long a 250 h.p. oil engine, working at full
load, would take to consume 200 lb. of the fuel.   One C.H.U. is
equivalent to 1400 ft. lb.   N.C.T.E.C.

(14) Describe, clearly, an experiment to determine the mechanical
equivalent of heat. Given that 1 h.p. = 746 watts and that 1 C.H.U.
= 1400 ft. lb., what is the electrical equivalent of heat supplied at the
rate of 1 C.H.U. per min. ? Give your answer in watts.

                                                                   N.C.T.E.C.

(15) An electrical generator has an output of 5 kilowatts. If 1 h.p.
= 746 watts, calculate the output of the generator in horsepower.
This output is 22% of the heat supplied by the fuel used by the
engine which drives the generator. How much fuel having a heating
value of 10,000 C.H.U. per lb. is consumed per hour ?   N.C.T.E.C.

(16) If heat at the rate of 200 C.H.U. per min. is applied to 200 lb.
of water contained in an open vessel at a temperature of 15° C., find
the time taken before 20 lb. of the water is converted into steam. Latent
heat of steam, 540 C.H.U. per lb.   N.C.T.E.C.

(17) A ship consumes for driving purposes 55 tons of oil per day of
24 hours.   One lb. of oil when burned gives out 10,300 C.H.U.   Find
how many foot-pounds of energy are available per min. and the
horsepower this represents.   .   ᵀJ.L.C.I.

CHAPTER 13

EXPANSION OF GASES

When we consider the changes in the volume of a gas we shall find that these can be produced by either a change in temperature or by a change in pressure or by changes in both at the same time. The usual method of restoring a bulged table tennis ball to its normal shape is by holding it near to a source of heat. The heat of a fire causes the air in the ball to expand and force out the bulge. It will be obvious that the bulge could not be straightened out unless the pressure in the ball increased relative to the outside. So the increased temperature has resulted in an increase in pressure and volume.

Again, if you close the valve connection of a cycle pump and force the piston handle into the pump, thus compressing the air inside the pump, you will find that the temperature of the air increases. You will have noticed that when you are inflating your cycle tyres the rubber connection becomes quite hot during the process. This means that the variation in volume due to increase in pressure is also accompanied by an increase in temperature. The engineer makes use of this fact in developing the Diesel engine such as is used on motor buses and heavy haulage wagons. The piston compresses the air inside the cylinder and at the same time increases its temperature to the region of 1000° F. A spray of oil which is then injected into the cylinder immediately ignites and explodes, thus forcing the piston back in the cylinder and consequently turning the crankshaft.

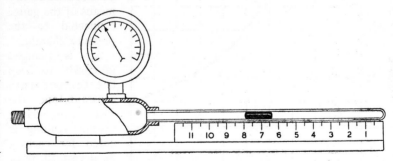

FIG. 87—EXPANSION OF GAS AT CONSTANT TEMPERATURE
The gas is trapped by the pellet of mercury in the closed tube. The pressure in the left hand cylinder is increased by means of a cycle pump. The pressure in this cylinder must always equal the pressure of the trapped gas. The volume of this gas is proportional to the length of the column as read from the scale. Pressure readings and scale readings are plotted in Fig. 88.

To study the changes which take place in the volume of a gas it will be most convenient, first, to keep the temperature constant and vary the pressure, and secondly, to keep the pressure constant and vary the temperature.

Relationship between Pressure and Volume of Gas. Constant Temperature

A piece of apparatus suitable for finding the relationship between the pressure and volume of a gas is shown in Fig. 87. A quantity of air is trapped in the closed end of a glass tube by means of a pellet of mercury. The open end of the tube is connected to a pressure chamber which is provided with a screwed nozzle suitable for connection to an ordinary cycle pump. As air is pumped into the chamber the pressure increases and the mercury is forced towards the closed end of the tube. The volume of the trapped air is thus reduced. A scale mounted near the tube indicates the length of the column of air and the scale reading can be taken as an indication of the volume of the air, since :

Volume = scale reading × cross-sectional area of bore.

The cross-sectional area of the bore is constant so the volume of the trapped area is proportional to the scale reading.

Now the pressure on either side of the mercury pellet is obviously the same. If this were not true then the pellet would be forced towards the lower pressure until the pressures became equalised. The pressure of the trapped air can thus be measured by means of the gauge connected to the pressure chamber.

Air is pumped in slowly to keep the temperature constant and the corresponding volume reading is noted for each 5 lb. per sq. in. pressure reading. The following results are of the type obtained from the experiment.

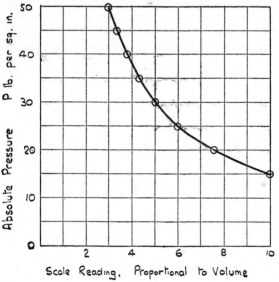

FIG. 88—PRESSURE-VOLUME GRAPH
For constant temperature expansion.

Pressure lb./sq. in. P	15	20	25	30	35	40	45	50
Scale Reading V ..	10	7·5	6·0	5·0	4·28	3·75	3·33	3·0

The results have been plotted in Fig. 88 and produce a smooth curve known as a "rectangular hyperbola." One feature of this curve is that it is gradually getting nearer to the horizontal and vertical axes although it never reaches either of them. This means that the volume can be made very small by a considerable increase in pressure, but the volume can never be reduced to zero. In terms of the apparatus shown in Fig. 87 the mercury pellet can never be forced to the end of the tube.

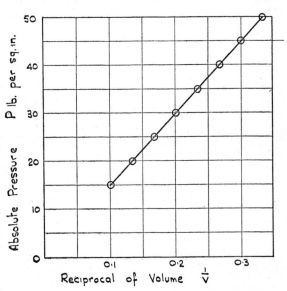

FIG. 89—P-V GRAPH PLOTTED ON A BASE OF $\dfrac{1}{V}$

The resulting graph is a straight line passing through the origin (if produced) showing that the absolute pressure is proportional to the reciprocal of the volume. In other words pressure is inversely proportional to volume.

An alternative method of plotting the results is shown in Fig. 89 where pressure is plotted against the reciprocal of the volume, i.e., against $\dfrac{1}{Volume}$

Pressure lb./sq. in. P	15	20	25	30	35	40	45	50
Scale Reading V ..	10	7·5	6·0	5·0	4·28	3·75	3·33	3·0
$\dfrac{1}{V}$	0·1	0·133	0·166	0·2	0·233	0·267	0·3	0·33

This method of plotting is useful because it tells immediately which of the results, if any, are inaccurate. But more than this, it leads us to the relationship between pressure and volume. *If we multiply the pressure reading and the scale reading together we shall find that they always give the same figure.* (When you do this experiment you will no doubt find that a slight variation occurs in the constant. You would in such a case take an average value.)

Pressure lb./sq. in. P	15	20	25	30	35	40	45	50
Scale Reading V ..	10	7·5	6·0	5·0	4·28	3·75	3·33	3·0
P × V	150	150	150	150	150	150	150	150

So if P_1 and V_1 indicate the pressure and the volume of a gas at one instant and P_2 and V_2 the corresponding values of the same gas at another instant then ;

$$P_1 V_1 = P_2 V_2 = \text{constant.}$$

This relationship was discovered by Sir Robert Boyle in the year 1661. It is usually stated as follows and is known as Boyle's Law :

The product of the pressure and the volume of a gas remains constant provided that the temperature is kept constant.

When the pressure and volume of a gas is allowed to change with the temperature remaining constant, the change is said to take place under " isothermal " conditions. **Isothermal means constant temperature.**

Absolute and Gauge Pressure

The reading given on most types of pressure gauges is not the actual pressure of the gas, but the difference between the pressure of the gas and the pressure of the atmosphere. The gauge reading is usually called the " gauge pressure " whilst the actual pressure is called the " absolute pressure." These two pressures are related by the formula :

Absolute pressure = gauge pressure + pressure of atmosphere.

The pressure of the atmosphere which varies from day to day and from place to place is taken as 14·7 lb. per sq. in. at sea level. It is usual at this stage to use 15 lb. per sq. in. as the value of atmospheric pressure. In the results which have been given of the experiment on Boyle's Law on page 159 the gauge pressures have been converted to absolute pressures. *In all questions on Boyle's Law and other gas laws, ABSOLUTE PRESSURES must be used.*

The pressure of the atmosphere is sometimes expressed in terms of the height of a column of mercury. The value at sea level is given as 76 cm. of mercury. This means that the pressure of the atmosphere is

sufficient to support a column of mercury 76 cm. high. If the mercury
had a cross-sectional area of 1 sq. in. then since 1 in. equals 2·54 cm. the
volume of the mercury would be $\frac{7\cdot6}{2\cdot54}$ × 1 cub. in.   One cub. in. of
mercury weighs 0·49 lb. therefore the weight of the mercury column
will be $\frac{7\cdot6}{2\cdot54}$ × 1 × 0·49 = 14·7 lb.   Since this weight is acting upon an
area of 1 sq. in. the pressure which it exerts is 14·7 lb. per sq. in.   This
is just balanced by the pressure of the atmosphere.

High Pressures

When dealing with high pressures an alternative unit of pressure is
used. It is the "atmosphere." As its name implies, it is taken as the
pressure of the atmosphere, usually 15 lb. per sq. in.   Thus a pressure
of 20 atmospheres is equivalent to 300 lb. per sq. in.

Relationship between Volume and Temperature of Gas.   Constant Pressure

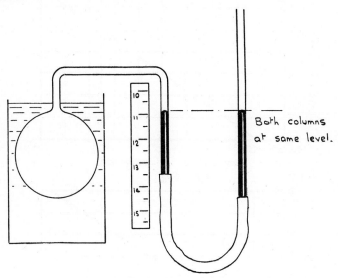

Both columns
at same level.

FIG. 90—EXPANSION OF GAS AT CONSTANT PRESSURE
The gas is contained in the flask.   The temperature of the gas is increased
by heating the surrounding water.   This causes the gas to expand and
force the mercury in the left hand column down   The right hand column
is then lowered until the level of the mercury is the same in both columns
This means that the pressure in each column is the same, and since the right
hand column is open to the atmosphere it will always be at atmospheric
pressure.   The scale reading is noted and plotted against the temperature
of the gas as in Fig. 91.

We shall find that it is rather more difficult to determine the relationship between temperature and volume when the pressure is kept constant.

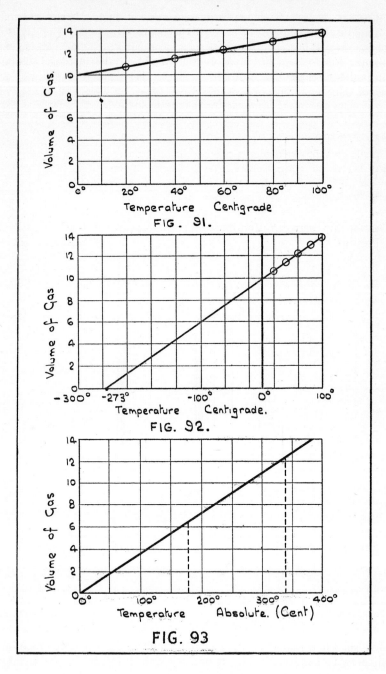

FIG. 91.

FIG. 92.

FIG. 93

A piece of apparatus which can be used to give an approximation to the law is shown in Fig. 90. The neck of a glass flask is connected by rubber tubing to an open-ended glass tube. Mercury is introduced into the tube and allowed to pass into the neck of the flask, thus trapping a quantity of air in the flask. The volume of the trapped air is given by reading the scale opposite the level of the mercury in the neck of the flask. The flask is inserted into a bath of water which is heated by a bunsen. As the temperature rises the volume of the air increases and the mercury is forced down the flask tube and up the open tube. In order to keep the pressure constant the level of the mercury in each tube must be the same. The open tube will therefore have to be raised or lowered to bring the two levels equal. The scale reading is then observed and tabulated against the temperature reading.

Temperature ° C.	..	20	40	60	80	100
Volume	.. ..	10·7	11·5	12·2	12·9	13·7

The results are shown graphically in Fig. 91 from which we draw the following conclusions.

(1) The results all lie on a straight line.

(2) The scale reading decreases uniformly as the temperature decreases and the graph suggests that if the temperature were reduced sufficiently the volume would be reduced to zero.

In Fig. 92 the results have been re-plotted to a different scale so that we can determine the temperature at which the volume would be zero. The graph is produced backwards until it cuts the zero volume line and the temperature is found to be − 273° C.

Up to the present we have not been able to reach this low temperature and there are reasons for believing that this will be the lowest temperature which it will be possible to reach.

Of course we must not expect to find that volume of the gas is actually zero at this low temperature. We shall find that it will have liquefied and solidified before this temperature is reached and will no longer obey a gas law.

Since − 273° C. is the lowest temperature which we can expect to reach it would seem that this would be useful to use as the zero point on a temperature scale instead of choosing a point such as the freezing point of water. We shall also find that there are great advantages in using this new zero point which is called the **ABSOLUTE ZERO**. Fig. 93 shows the same graph as Fig. 92, with the exception that the temperature scale has been altered. − 273° on the first graph is taken as the zero mark on the second graph so that the figures on the second graph are 273 higher than on the first graph. These amended temperatures are called **ABSOLUTE TEMPERATURES**.

For example: $-273°$ C. $=$ $0°$ C. absolute
$$0° \text{ C.} = 273° \text{ C. absolute}$$
$$50° \text{ C.} = 323° \text{ C. absolute}$$
$$100° \text{ C.} = 373° \text{ C. absolute.}$$

Now from the graph in Fig. 93 the volume corresponding to
$$100° \text{ C. absolute is } 3·66$$
$$200° \text{ C. absolute is } 7·32$$
$$300° \text{ C. absolute is } 10·98$$

i.e., when the absolute temperature is doubled the volume is doubled, when the absolute temperature is trebled the volume is trebled.

Notice that this only applies if we use the absolute temperatures. It is this fact that makes the absolute temperature so important.

Let V_1 be the volume of the gas at $T_1°$ absolute
V_2 be the volume of the gas at $T_2°$ absolute

then from the graph we see that the value of $\frac{V_1}{T_1}$ is equal to the slope of the line, or to the tangent of the angle which the line makes with the horizontal. But $\frac{V_2}{T_2}$ is also equal to the tangent of the same angle.

$$\therefore \frac{V_1}{T_1} = \frac{V_2}{T_2} = \text{constant}$$

Remember—Always use ABSOLUTE TEMPERATURES.

This is the important law connecting volume and temperature of a gas when the pressure remains constant. It was first discovered by a scientist named Charles and is often referred to as Charles's Law. It can be stated in two forms:

(1) The volume of a gas is directly proportional to the absolute temperature when the pressure remains constant.

(By directly proportional we simply mean that if you double one you double the other, if you halve one you halve the other and so on.)

(2) The volume of a gas increases by $\frac{1}{273}$ of its volume at $0°$ C. for every degree Centigrade rise in temperature (corresponding figures for Fahrenheit are: $\frac{1}{492}$ of its volume at $32°$ F. for every degree Fahrenheit rise in temperature).

The second form is simply another way of saying that the coefficient of expansion (cubical, since we are dealing with volumes) of a gas at constant pressure is $\frac{1}{273}$ per degree Centigrade or $\frac{1}{492}$ per degree Fahrenheit.

Fahrenheit Scale and Absolute Temperatures

If a temperature is given in degrees Fahrenheit it can be converted into absolute Fahrenheit degrees by adding $460°$. In other words, the absolute zero on the Fahrenheit scale is $-460°$ F.

Relationship between Pressure, Volume, and Temperature of a Gas

In practice, whenever the state of a gas is undergoing a change, we shall generally find that pressure, volume, and temperature are all changing simultaneously. Let us try to determine the law involving all three conditions. If you find it difficult to follow the reasoning at first, then carefully re-read making sure that each step is clear.

Fig. 94A is a cylinder containing a quantity of gas under a loaded piston which is free to move in the cylinder. The pressure temperature, and volume of the gas are P_1, V_1 and T_1. (Pressures and temperatures all being absolute.) In diagram C the pressure and temperature have been changed to P_2 and T_2 respectively so that the new volume is V_2.

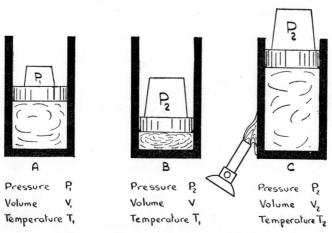

A
Pressure P_1
Volume V_1
Temperature T_1

B
Pressure P_2
Volume V
Temperature T_1

C
Pressure P_2
Volume V_2
Temperature T_2

FIG. 94—GENERAL EXPANSION OF GAS

Original conditions are given in A. Pressure is increased with a corresponding decrease in volume while the temperature is kept constant (B). The pressure is then kept constant and the temperature is increased (C). The relationship between the original and final conditions is given by

$$\frac{P_1 V_1}{T_1} = \frac{P_2 V_2}{T_2}$$

Let us think of the change taking place in two stages.

Stage (i) Change the pressure from P_1 to P_2, keeping the temperature constant at T_1.

Stage (ii) Change the temperature from T_1 to T_2, keeping the pressure constant at P_2.

We know the laws governing each of these changes.

Stage (i) A heavier weight is put on the piston in order to compress the gas to a pressure P_2. The compression must be done slowly so that the temperature remains constant at T_1. Let the new volume be denoted by V. Then by Boyle's Law $P_1 V_1 = P_2 V$ from which we get the new volume:

$$V = \frac{P_1 V_1}{P_2} \quad \dots\dots\dots\dots\dots\dots(1)$$

Stage (ii) Keeping the same weight on the piston so that the pressure remains at P_2, the temperature of the gas is increased from T_1 to T_2. The gas expands and the piston and weight are forced up the cylinder till the volume of the gas becomes V_2. Since the change takes place at constant pressure we can apply Charles's Law.

$$\text{Initial volume} = V$$
$$\text{Initial temperature} = T_1$$
$$\text{Final volume} = V_2$$
$$\text{Final temperature} = T_2$$

$$\frac{V}{T_1} = \frac{V_2}{T_2} \text{ which gives } V_2 = \frac{T_2 V}{T_1}$$

Substitute the value of V from (1)

$$V_2 = \frac{T_2}{T_1} \cdot \frac{P_1 V_1}{P_2}$$

Multiply both sides by $\dfrac{P_2}{T_2}$

$$\frac{P_2 V_2}{T_2} = \frac{P_1 V_1}{T_1}$$

Or in its more usual form

$$\frac{P_1 V_1}{T_1} = \frac{P_2 V_2}{T_2}$$

Example 73.—A cylinder contains 40 cub. ft. of oxygen at 450 lb. per sq. in. gauge. Determine its volume when expanded to 185 lb. per sq. in. gauge if the temperature remains the same. In this case the law of the expansion is $P_1 V_1 = P_2 V_1$
$P_1 = 450 + 15 = 465$ lb. per sq. in. absolute.
$V_1 = 40 \times 1728$ cub. in.
$P_2 = 185 + 15 = 200$ lb. per sq. in. absolute.
$V_2 = ?$
$P_1 V_1 = P_2 V_2$
$465 \times 40 \times 1728 = 200 \times V_2 \times 1728$

$$V_2 = \frac{465 \times 40 \times 1728}{200 \times 1728}$$

$V_2 = 93$ cub. ft.
Final volume is 93 cub. ft.   **Ans.**

Example 74.—Steam is admitted to a cylinder of a steam engine at a pressure of 80 lb. per sq. in. gauge. The steam supply is cut off when the piston has travelled through one third of the stroke. Calculate the pressure of the steam when the piston is at half stroke and at the end of the stroke.

Let V == the volume of the cylinder.

Then at $\frac{1}{3}$ stroke the volume will be $\dfrac{V}{3}$

(a) *At half stroke*

$$P_1 = 80 + 15 = 95 \text{ lb. sq. in. absolute.} \qquad P_2 = ?$$

$$V_1 = \frac{V}{3} \qquad\qquad\qquad\qquad V_2 = \frac{V}{2}$$

$$P_1 V_1 = P_2 V_2$$

$$95 \times \frac{V}{3} = P_2 \frac{V}{2}$$

$$P_2 = \frac{95 \times 2}{3} = 63\tfrac{1}{3} \text{ lb. per sq. in. absolute.}$$

$$= 48\tfrac{1}{3} \text{ lb. per sq. in. gauge. } \textbf{Ans.}$$

(b) *At end of stroke*

$$P_1 = 95 \text{ lb. per sq. in. absolute.} \qquad P_3 = ?$$

$$V_1 = \frac{V}{3} \qquad\qquad\qquad\qquad V_3 = V.$$

$$P_1 V_1 = P_3 V_3$$

$$95 \times \frac{V}{3} = P_3 V$$

$$P_3 = \frac{95}{3} = 31\tfrac{2}{3} \text{ lb. per sq. in. absolute.}$$

$$= 16\tfrac{2}{3} \text{ lb. per sq. in. gauge. } \textbf{Ans.}$$

Example 75.—20 cub. ft. of a gas are heated at constant pressure until the volume is 60 cub. ft. If the original temperature was 60° C. what is the final temperature ?

Since the pressure is constant we can use the law :

$$\frac{V_1}{T_1} = \frac{V_2}{T_2}$$

$$V_1 = 20 \qquad\qquad\qquad\qquad V_2 = 60$$

$$T_1 = 60 + 273 = 333° \text{ C. absolute.} \qquad T_2 = ?$$

$$\frac{V_1}{T_1} = \frac{V_2}{T_2}$$

$$\frac{20}{333} = \frac{60}{T_2} \qquad T_2 = \frac{333 \times 60}{20} = 999° \text{ C. absolute.}$$

$$\text{Final temperature} = 999 - 273$$

$$= 726° \text{ C. } \textbf{Ans.}$$

Example 76.—Reduce 200 cub. ft. of gas at 20° C. and 60 lb. per sq. in. absolute to its volume at N.T.P.

$$P_1 = 60 \text{ lb. per sq. in.} \qquad P_2 = 15 \text{ lb. per sq. in.}$$

$$V_1 = 200 \times 1728 \text{ cub. in.} \qquad V_2 = ?$$

$$T_1 = 20 + 273 = 293° \text{ C. abs.} \quad T_1 = 0 + 273 = 273° \text{ C. abs.}$$

$$\frac{P_1 V_1}{T_1} = \frac{P_2 V_2}{T_9}$$

$$\frac{60 \times 200 \times 1728}{293} = \frac{15 \times V_2 \times 1728}{273}$$

$$V_2 = \frac{60 \times 200 \times 1728 \times 273}{15 \times 1728 \times 293}$$

$$= 745 \text{ cub. ft.}$$

Volume of gas at N.T.P. = 745 cub. ft. Ans.

Example 77.—A gas container shows a pressure of 40 atmospheres when the temperature of the gas is 45° F. If the temperature is increased to 55° F. what will be the increase of the pressure ?

Since the gas is in a container its volume will remain constant.

$P_1 = 40$ atmospheres $\qquad P_2 = ?$

$T_1 = 45 + 460$ $\qquad\qquad T_2 = 55 + 460$

$\quad = 505°$ F. absolute. $\qquad = 515°$ F. absolute.

$$\frac{P_1}{T_1} = \frac{P_2}{T_2}$$

$$\frac{40}{505} = \frac{P_2}{515} \qquad \therefore P_2 = \frac{515 \times 40}{505} = 40{\cdot}792 \text{ atmospheres.}$$

Increase in pressure $=\quad 0{\cdot}792$ atmospheres

$$= 0{\cdot}792 \times 15 \text{ lb. per sq. in.}$$

$$= 11{\cdot}9 \text{ lb. per sq. in. Ans.}$$

Example 78.—4 cub. ft. of air at 500 lb. per sq. in. absolute and 30° C. expands to 8 cub. ft. when the pressure is 100 lb. per sq. in. absolute. Calculate the change in temperature.

N.C.T.E.C.

$P_1 = 500$ lb. per sq. in. $\qquad P_2 = 100$ lb. per sq. in.

$V_1 = 4 \times 1728$ cub. in. $\qquad V_2 = 8 \times 1728$ cub. in.

$T_1 = 30 + 273 = 303°$ C. abs. $\qquad T_2 = ?$

$$\frac{P_1 V_1}{T_1} = \frac{P_2 V_2}{T_2}$$

$$\frac{500 \times 4 \times 1728}{303} = \frac{100 \times 8 \times 1728}{T_2}$$

$$T_2 = \frac{303 \times 100 \times 8 \times 1728}{500 \times 4 \times 1728} = 121{\cdot}2° \text{ C. abs.}$$

$$= 121{\cdot}2 - 273$$

$$= -151{\cdot}8° \text{ C.}$$

The temperature falls by 181·8° C. Ans.

EXERCISE 12

(All pressures are given as absolute except otherwise stated.)

(1) The volume of gas in an engine cylinder is 1 cub. ft. at 15 lb. per

sq. in. pressure and 17° C. temperature. What will the volume become when the pressure and the temperature are increased to 100 lb. per sq. in. (absolute) and 67° C.?

(2) Complete the following table. Atmospheric pressure 15 lb. per sq. in.

Gauge pressure	30	70	100	180					
Absolute pressure ..	45	85	115		17	27	72	95	135

All the values are in lb. per sq. in.

(3) A cylinder contains 10 cub. ft. of oxygen at 400 lb. per sq. in. gauge. Determine its volume when expanded to (a) 200 lb. per sq. in. gauge, (b) 85 lb. per sq. in. gauge, and (c) atmospheric pressure.

(4) A steam engine cylinder contains $1\frac{1}{2}$ cub. ft. of steam at 120 lb. per sq. in. gauge. If the steam obeys Boyle's Law, find the volume when the pressure has dropped to 11 lb. per sq. in. below the atmosphere. At what pressure (absolute) will the volume be 2 cub. ft.?

(5) A cylinder contains 5 cub. ft. of gas at atmospheric pressure and 117° C. Find its volume at 27° C. when the pressure is 40 lb. per sq. in. absolute.

(6) Determine the volume at 60 lb. per sq. in. absolute and 30° C. of a certain mass of gas which has a volume at N.T.P. of 50 cub. ft.

(7) A gas container, on being raised in temperature from 15° C. to 20° C. shows an increase in pressure of 0.6 atmospheres. What would be the pressure when the temperature was raised to 35° C. assuming that the volume of the container remains constant?

(8) The volume of 1 gram of nitrogen at 20° C. and a pressure of 76 cm. of mercury is 860 c.c. What volume would it occupy at 57 cm. of mercury and 500° C?

(9) Reduce 100 cub. ft. of gas at 15° C. and 50 lb. per sq. in. to its volume at N.T.P.

(10) A compressed air container has a capacity of 280 cub. ft. and contains air at 29° C. and a pressure of 120 lb. per sq. in. absolute. Find the volume this air will occupy at N.T.P. Find also the weight of the air if 1 cub. ft. of air at N.T.P. weighs 0·0807 lb.

(11) A quantity of gas originally occupies 9 cub. ft. at 40 lb. per sq. in. absolute pressure and 127° C. It is heated and allowed to expand till its volume and temperature are respectively 18 cub. ft. and 227° C. Find its new absolute pressure.

(12) An air compressor is to compress 120 cub. ft. of air at normal atmospheric pressure of 14·7 lb. per sq. in. into a receiver having a capacity

of 15 cub. ft. Determine the resulting pressure in the receiver after the temperature has cooled down to that of the atmosphere.

If now the air is further compressed until the pressure is 200 lb. per sq. in., determine the new volume of the air if no change in temperature takes place.

(13) If steam be admitted into the cylinder of a steam engine at a pressure of 75 lb. per sq. in. above that of the atmosphere (15 lb. per sq. in.) and the cut off is one-third of the stroke, calculate the pressures at half, three-quarters, and end of the stroke. Draw to scale a diagram which shows how the pressure varies during the stroke. U.L.C.I.

(14) State Charles's Law for a perfect gas.

If 10 cub. ft. of a gas initially at 100° C. are heated at constant pressure until the volume is doubled, what will be the final temperature ?

N.C.T.E.C.

(15) What do you understand by the terms " absolute pressure " and " absolute temperature " ?

State Boyle's and Charles's Laws and show that they may be expressed in the form of a single equation. Find the volume of air at 14·7 lb. per sq. in. absolute and 50° C. which is at 70 lb. per sq. in. absolute and 64° C. when compressed into a reservoir of 750 cub. ft. capacity.

N.C.T.E.C.

(16) Compressed air at 120 lb. per sq. in. absolute and 30° C. passes through a heater which raises its temperature to 100° C. If the pressure falls to 110 lb. per sq. in. absolute find the percentage change in volume.

N.C.T.E.C.

CHAPTER 14

WRITING UP THE EXPERIMENT

Finally there are one or two points in connection with experimental work which should be mentioned. All students of Mechanical Engineering Science will have some experimental work to do, in fact many authorities give their considered opinion that experimental work should form the basis of the course of studies. The object of experimental work is to verify one or other of the important principles which have been indicated in this book. It is not anticipated that you will discover some new thing, but rather that you will deduce some established principle. For example, certain important ideas have been given in the chapter on Friction relating to the force of friction. No attempt was made to prove these ideas to be correct. In fact it would be exceedingly difficult, if not impossible, to establish any proof. The ideas have been formulated as a result of much experimental work. They can also be shown to be reasonably true by further experiment. The object of the experiment would be to determine the relationship between the weight of the moving body and the force which is just sufficient to move it over a horizontal surface.

It is very important that we should give the same attention to " writing up " the experiment as we do to carrying it out. A well-kept laboratory note book is just as valuable as a set of lecture notes. There is one important idea which you should keep in mind when you are writing up the experiment.

Make sure that your information is sufficiently complete and your description sufficiently clear to enable any of your fellow students to carry out the experiment without any other reference than to your account of the experiment.

This is a very safe guide.

Layout of Experiment Account

The layout of the report will in most cases comprise the following headings :

(1) **Object.**—A clear statement as to the reason for doing experiment.

(2) **Apparatus.**—This will include brief description together with explanatory diagrams.

(3) **Method.**—A detailed account of the things you did, the precautions you took, the readings you observed.

(4) **Results.**—All your readings should be given, together with a specimen of any calculation which you have had to make. If any graphs have to be prepared they should be included under this heading.

(5) **Conclusions or Deductions.**

In some of the later experimental work which you will have to do it is also advisable to give an account of the theory on which the experiment depends. This is usually inserted after " object."

Style of Writing

Always write in the past tense. Describe the experiment as something which has been done. Avoid mere copying from an instruction sheet. Use your own words. Cut out all personal references. Do not write :
" Then I placed the weights in the scale pan and Tom altered the angle of the plane."
Write it like this :
" Weights were placed in the scale pan and the angle of the plane was altered."

Diagrams

A neat diagram will often save considerable descriptive matter, particularly when describing the apparatus. But remember it must be a **NEAT** diagram. *Apply the lessons which you learn in the Engineering Drawing Class.* So many students produce very neat drawings in that class but produce most unsatisfactory drawings in the other classes.

Calculations

There is no need to fill your laboratory book with calculations. You should give one specimen calculation of each type that you do. There is no excuse for remarking at a later date when you refer to your workings " I wonder where this figure comes from."

Conclusions

The very common conclusion which reads " The law was verified " is useless. You must at least state the law, even though this has already been done under " object." It is much more satisfactory to write your conclusion in this manner :
" The results indicate that the clockwise moments about either support are equal to the anticlockwise moments about the same support. The slight differences between the two values are due to experimental errors arising from : (1) Spring balance readings ; and (2) Metre rule measurements of the position of the weights on the beam."
A typical account of an experiment will serve to emphasise some of the points just made.

Experiment No........   Date...............

The Inclined Plane

OBJECT.—To determine the force, acting parallel to the plane, required to maintain a roller in equilibrium on the smooth inclined plane.

APPARATUS.—Smooth inclined plane ; roller of known weight ; string, scale pan, and weights ; plumb bob and rule.

The arrangement of the apparatus is shown in the diagram.

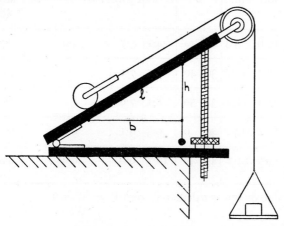

DIAGRAM OF APPARATUS

The roller should run as freely as possible over the surface of the plane. The bearings of both the roller and the pulley were lubricated before commencing the experiment.

METHOD.—The plane was adjusted to a convenient angle. Weights were added to the scale pan until the roller just began to move up the plane with uniform motion. The total force (P_1) pulling the roller is the sum of the weights in the pan and the weight of the scale pan itself. Some of the weights were then removed from the pan until the roller began to move down the plane with uniform motion. The pull in the cord, which is the sum of the weights and the weight of the scale pan, is referred to as P_2. The mean of these two values was taken as the correct force (P) required to hold the roller in equilibrium on the plane.

The weight of the roller was obtained by a spring balance.

To determine the inclination of the plane the lengths l and b were measured, the latter with the aid of a plumb bob. The height h was calculated. After these observations had been made the experiment was repeated four times using different inclinations of the plane.

RESULTS :

Weight of scale pan = 0·7 lb.
Weight of roller   = 13·8 lb.

$$\cos \theta = \frac{b}{l}$$

No.	l in.	b in.	h in.	θ	P_1 lb.	P_2 lb.	$P = \dfrac{P_1+P_2}{2}$ lb.	P calcu-lated lb.	R lb. calcu-lated
1	20	18·6	5·4	15° 40′	4·1	3·7	3·9	3·73	12·8
2	20	17·2	10·2	30° 40′	7·5	7·1	7·25	7·05	11·9
3	20	16·4	11·4₂	34° 50′	8·1	7·9	8	7·9	11·3
4	20	15·1	13·1	40° 0′	9·3	9·1	9·2	9·05	10·4
5	20	14·0	14·3	45° 40′	10·1	9·8	9·95	9·88	9·6

The value of P was calculated from

$$P = W\sin\theta$$
$$= \frac{Wh}{l}$$
$$= \frac{13\cdot8h}{l} \text{ lb.}$$

The value of R was calculated from

$$R = W\cos\theta$$
$$= \frac{Wb}{l}$$
$$= \frac{13\cdot8b}{l} \text{ lb.}$$

Example No. 2

$$P = \frac{13\cdot8 \times 10\cdot2}{20} = 7\cdot05 \text{ lb.}$$

$$R = \frac{13\cdot8 \times 17\cdot2}{20} = 11\cdot9 \text{ lb.}$$

Conclusions

(1) The force required to hold the roller in equilibrium on the plane is proportional to the sine of the angle of inclination of the plane. Expressed in ratio form:

$$\frac{P}{W} = \frac{b}{l}$$

(2) The differences between the observed and calculated values are due to:

(a) Experimental error arising from inaccurate measurement of the lengths.

(b) Friction at the bearings of the roller and the pulley.

In no case does the difference exceed 5% of the calculated value.

LOGARITHMS.

No.	Log.	1	2	3	4	5	6	7	8	9	1	2	3	4	5	6	7	8	9
1·0	·0000	0043	0086	0128	0170	0212	0253	0294	0334	0374	4	8	12	17	21	25	29	33	37
1·1	·0414	0453	0492	0531	0569	0607	0645	0682	0719	0755	4	8	11	15	19	23	26	30	34
1·2	·0792	0828	0864	0899	0934	0969	1004	1038	1072	1106	3	7	10	14	17	21	24	28	31
1·3	·1139	1173	1206	1239	1271	1303	1335	1367	1399	1430	3	6	10	13	16	19	23	26	29
1·4	·1461	1492	1523	1553	1584	1614	1644	1673	1703	1732	3	6	9	12	15	18	21	24	27
1·5	·1761	1790	1818	1847	1875	1903	1931	1959	1987	2014	3	6	8	11	14	17	20	22	25
1·6	·2041	2068	2095	2122	2148	2175	2201	2227	2253	2279	3	5	8	11	13	16	18	21	24
1·7	·2304	2330	2355	2380	2405	2430	2455	2480	2504	2529	2	5	7	10	12	15	17	20	22
1·8	·2553	2577	2601	2625	2648	2672	2695	2718	2742	2765	2	5	7	9	12	14	16	19	21
1·9	·2788	2810	2833	2856	2878	2900	2923	2945	2967	2989	2	4	7	9	11	13	16	18	20
2·0	·3010	3032	3054	3075	3096	3118	3139	3160	3181	3201	2	4	6	8	11	13	15	17	19
2·1	·3222	3243	3263	3284	3304	3324	3345	3365	3385	3404	2	4	6	8	10	12	14	16	18
2·2	·3424	3444	3464	3483	3502	3522	3541	3560	3579	3598	2	4	6	8	10	12	14	15	17
2·3	·3617	3636	3655	3674	3692	3711	3729	3747	3766	3784	2	4	6	7	9	11	13	15	17
2·4	·3802	3820	3838	3856	3874	3892	3909	3927	3945	3962	2	4	5	7	9	11	12	14	16
2·5	·3979	3997	4014	4031	4048	4065	4082	4099	4116	4133	2	3	5	7	9	10	12	14	15
2·6	·4150	4166	4183	4200	4216	4232	4249	4265	4281	4298	2	3	5	7	8	10	11	13	15
2·7	·4314	4330	4346	4362	4378	4393	4409	4425	4440	4456	2	3	5	6	8	9	11	13	14
2·8	·4472	4487	4502	4518	4533	4548	4564	4579	4594	4609	2	3	5	6	8	9	11	12	14
2·9	·4624	4639	4654	4669	4683	4698	4713	4728	4742	4757	1	3	4	6	7	9	10	12	13
3·0	·4771	4786	4800	4814	4829	4843	4857	4871	4886	4900	1	3	4	6	7	9	10	11	13
3·1	·4914	4928	4942	4955	4969	4983	4997	5011	5024	5038	1	3	4	6	7	8	10	11	12
3·2	·5051	5065	5079	5092	5105	5119	5132	5145	5159	5172	1	3	4	5	7	8	9	11	12
3·3	·5185	5198	5211	5224	5237	5250	5263	5276	5289	5302	1	3	4	5	6	8	9	10	12
3·4	·5315	5328	5340	5353	5366	5378	5391	5403	5416	5428	1	3	4	5	6	8	9	10	11
3·5	·5441	5453	5465	5478	5490	5502	5514	5527	5539	5551	1	2	4	5	6	7	9	10	11
3·6	·5563	5575	5587	5599	5611	5623	5635	5647	5658	5670	1	2	4	5	6	7	8	10	11
3·7	·5682	5694	5705	5717	5729	5740	5752	5763	5775	5786	1	2	3	5	6	7	8	9	10
3·8	·5798	5809	5821	5832	5843	5855	5866	5877	5888	5899	1	2	3	5	6	7	8	9	10
3·9	·5911	5922	5933	5944	5955	5966	5977	5988	5999	6010	1	2	3	4	5	7	8	9	10
4·0	·6021	6031	6042	6053	6064	6075	6085	6096	6107	6117	1	2	3	4	5	6	8	9	10
4·1	·6128	6138	6149	6160	6170	6180	6191	6201	6212	6222	1	2	3	4	5	6	7	8	9
4·2	·6232	6243	6253	6263	6274	6284	6294	6304	6314	6325	1	2	3	4	5	6	7	8	9
4·3	·6335	6345	6355	6365	6375	6385	6395	6405	6415	6425	1	2	3	4	5	6	7	8	9
4·4	·6435	6444	6454	6464	6474	6484	6493	6503	6513	6522	1	2	3	4	5	6	7	8	9
4·5	·6532	6542	6551	6561	6571	6580	6590	6599	6609	6618	1	2	3	4	5	6	7	8	9
4·6	·6628	6637	6646	6656	6665	6675	6684	6693	6702	6712	1	2	3	4	5	6	7	7	8
4·7	·6721	6730	6739	6749	6758	6767	6776	6785	6794	6803	1	2	3	4	5	5	6	7	8
4·8	·6812	6821	6830	6839	6848	6857	6866	6875	6884	6893	1	2	3	4	4	5	6	7	8
4·9	·6902	6911	6920	6928	6937	6946	6955	6964	6972	6981	1	2	3	4	4	5	6	7	8
5·0	·6990	6998	7007	7016	7024	7033	7042	7050	7059	7067	1	2	3	3	4	5	6	7	8
5·1	·7076	7084	7093	7101	7110	7118	7126	7135	7143	7152	1	2	3	3	4	5	6	7	8
5·2	·7160	7168	7177	7185	7193	7202	7210	7218	7226	7235	1	2	2	3	4	5	6	7	7
5·3	·7243	7251	7259	7267	7275	7284	7292	7300	7308	7316	1	2	2	3	4	5	6	6	7
5·4	·7324	7332	7340	7348	7356	7364	7372	7380	7388	7396	1	2	2	3	4	5	6	6	7

LOGARITHMS.

No.	Log.	1	2	3	4	5	6	7	8	9	1	2	3	4	5	6	7	8	9
5·5	·7404	7412	7419	7427	7435	7443	7451	7459	7466	7474	1	2	2	3	4	5	5	6	7
5·6	·7482	7490	7497	7505	7513	7520	7528	7536	7543	7551	1	2	2	3	4	5	5	6	7
5·7	·7559	7566	7574	7582	7589	7597	7604	7612	7619	7627	1	2	2	3	4	5	5	6	7
5·8	·7634	7642	7649	7657	7664	7672	7679	7686	7694	7701	1	1	2	3	4	4	5	6	7
5·9	·7709	7716	7723	7731	7738	7745	7752	7760	7767	7774	1	1	2	3	4	4	5	6	7
6·0	·7782	7789	7796	7803	7810	7818	7825	7832	7839	7846	1	1	2	3	4	4	5	6	6
6·1	·7853	7860	7868	7875	7882	7889	7896	7903	7910	7917	1	1	2	3	4	4	5	6	6
6·2	·7924	7931	7938	7945	7952	7959	7966	7973	7980	7987	1	1	2	3	3	4	5	6	6
6·3	·7993	8000	8007	8014	8021	8028	8035	8041	8048	8055	1	1	2	3	3	4	5	5	6
6·4	·8062	8069	8075	8082	8089	8096	8102	8109	8116	8122	1	1	2	3	3	4	5	5	6
6·5	·8129	8136	8142	8149	8156	8162	8169	8176	8182	8189	1	1	2	3	3	4	5	5	6
6·6	·8195	8202	8209	8215	8222	8228	8235	8241	8248	8254	1	1	2	3	3	4	5	5	6
6·7	·8261	8267	8274	8280	8287	8293	8299	8306	8312	8319	1	1	2	3	3	4	5	5	6
6·8	·8325	8331	8338	8344	8351	8357	8363	8370	8376	8382	1	1	2	3	3	4	4	5	6
6·9	·8388	8395	8401	8407	8414	8420	8426	8432	8439	8445	1	1	2	2	3	4	4	5	6
7·0	·8451	8457	8463	8470	8476	8482	8488	8494	8500	8506	1	1	2	2	3	4	4	5	6
7·1	·8513	8519	8525	8531	8537	8543	8549	8555	8561	8567	1	1	2	2	3	4	4	5	5
7·2	·8573	8579	8585	8591	8597	8603	8609	8615	8621	8627	1	1	2	2	3	4	4	5	5
7·3	·8633	8639	8645	8651	8657	8663	8669	8675	8681	8686	1	1	2	2	3	4	4	5	5
7·4	·8692	8698	8704	8710	8716	8722	8727	8733	8739	8745	1	1	2	2	3	4	4	5	5
7·5	·8751	8756	8762	8768	8774	8779	8785	8791	8797	8802	1	1	2	2	3	3	4	5	5
7·6	·8808	8814	8820	8825	8831	8837	8842	8848	8854	8859	1	1	2	2	3	3	4	5	5
7·7	·8865	8871	8876	8882	8887	8893	8899	8904	8910	8915	1	1	2	2	3	3	4	4	5
7·8	·8921	8927	8932	8938	8943	8949	8954	8960	8965	8971	1	1	2	2	3	3	4	4	5
7·9	·8976	8982	8987	8993	8998	9004	9009	9015	9020	9025	1	1	2	2	3	3	4	4	5
8·0	·9031	9036	9042	9047	9053	9058	9063	9069	9074	9079	1	1	2	2	3	3	4	4	5
8·1	·9085	9090	9096	9101	9106	9112	9117	9122	9128	9133	1	1	2	2	3	3	4	4	5
8·2	·9138	9143	9149	9154	9159	9165	9170	9175	9180	9186	1	1	2	2	3	3	4	4	5
8·3	·9191	9196	9201	9206	9212	9217	9222	9227	9232	9238	1	1	2	2	3	3	4	4	5
8·4	·9243	9248	9253	9258	9263	9269	9274	9279	9284	9289	1	1	2	2	3	3	4	4	5
8·5	·9294	9299	9304	9309	9315	9320	9325	9330	9335	9340	1	1	2	2	3	3	4	4	5
8·6	·9345	9350	9355	9360	9365	9370	9375	9380	9385	9390	1	1	2	2	3	3	4	4	5
8·7	·9395	9400	9405	9410	9415	9420	9425	9430	9435	9440	0	1	1	2	2	3	3	4	4
8·8	·9445	9450	9455	9460	9465	9469	9474	9479	9484	9489	0	1	1	2	2	3	3	4	4
8·9	·9494	9499	9504	9509	9513	9518	9523	9528	9533	9538	0	1	1	2	2	3	3	4	4
9·0	·9542	9547	9552	9557	9562	9566	9571	9576	9581	9586	0	1	1	2	2	3	3	4	4
9·1	·9590	9595	9600	9605	9609	9614	9619	9624	9628	9633	0	1	1	2	2	3	3	4	4
9·2	·9638	9643	9647	9652	9657	9661	9666	9671	9675	9680	0	1	1	2	2	3	3	4	4
9·3	·9685	9689	9694	9699	9703	9708	9713	9717	9722	9727	0	1	1	2	2	3	3	4	4
9·4	·9731	9736	9741	9745	9750	9754	9759	9763	9768	9773	0	1	1	2	2	3	3	4	4
9·5	·9777	9782	9786	9791	9795	9800	9805	9809	9814	9818	0	1	1	2	2	3	3	4	4
9·6	·9823	9827	9832	9836	9841	9845	9850	9854	9859	9863	0	1	1	2	2	3	3	4	4
9·7	·9868	9872	9877	9881	9886	9890	9894	9899	9903	9908	0	1	1	2	2	3	3	4	4
9·8	·9912	9917	9921	9926	9930	9934	9939	9943	9948	9952	0	1	1	2	2	3	3	4	4
9·9	·9956	9961	9965	9969	9974	9978	9983	9987	9991	9996	0	1	1	2	2	3	3	3	4

ANTI-LOGARITHMS.

Log.	0	1	2	3	4	5	6	7	8	9	1	2	3	4	5	6	7	8	9
·00	1000	1002	1005	1007	1009	1012	1014	1016	1019	1021	0	0	1	1	1	1	2	2	2
·01	1023	1026	1028	1030	1033	1035	1038	1040	1042	1045	0	0	1	1	1	1	2	2	2
·02	1047	1050	1052	1054	1057	1059	1062	1064	1067	1069	0	0	1	1	1	1	2	2	2
·03	1072	1074	1076	1079	1081	1084	1086	1089	1091	1094	0	0	1	1	1	1	2	2	2
·04	1096	1099	1102	1104	1107	1109	1112	1114	1117	1119	0	1	1	1	1	2	2	2	2
·05	1122	1125	1127	1130	1132	1135	1138	1140	1143	1146	0	1	1	1	1	2	2	2	2
·06	1148	1151	1153	1156	1159	1161	1164	1167	1169	1172	0	1	1	1	1	2	2	2	2
·07	1175	1178	1180	1183	1186	1189	1191	1194	1197	1199	0	1	1	1	1	2	2	2	2
·08	1202	1205	1208	1211	1213	1216	1219	1222	1225	1227	0	1	1	1	1	2	2	2	3
·09	1230	1233	1236	1239	1242	1245	1247	1250	1253	1256	0	1	1	1	1	2	2	2	3
·10	1259	1262	1265	1268	1271	1274	1276	1279	1282	1285	0	1	1	1	1	2	2	2	3
·11	1288	1291	1294	1297	1300	1303	1306	1309	1312	1315	0	1	1	1	2	2	2	2	3
·12	1318	1321	1324	1327	1330	1334	1337	1340	1343	1346	0	1	1	1	2	2	2	2	3
·13	1349	1352	1355	1358	1361	1365	1368	1371	1374	1377	0	1	1	1	2	2	2	3	3
·14	1380	1384	1387	1390	1393	1396	1400	1403	1406	1409	0	1	1	1	2	2	2	3	3
·15	1413	1416	1419	1422	1426	1429	1432	1435	1439	1442	0	1	1	1	2	2	2	3	3
·16	1445	1449	1452	1455	1459	1462	1466	1469	1472	1476	0	1	1	1	2	2	2	3	3
·17	1479	1483	1486	1489	1493	1496	1500	1503	1507	1510	0	1	1	1	2	2	2	3	3
·18	1514	1517	1521	1524	1528	1531	1535	1538	1542	1545	0	1	1	1	2	2	2	3	3
·19	1549	1552	1556	1560	1563	1567	1570	1574	1578	1581	0	1	1	1	2	2	3	3	3
·20	1585	1589	1592	1596	1600	1603	1607	1611	1614	1618	0	1	1	1	2	2	3	3	3
·21	1622	1626	1629	1633	1637	1641	1644	1648	1652	1656	0	1	1	2	2	2	3	3	3
·22	1660	1663	1667	1671	1675	1679	1683	1687	1690	1694	0	1	1	2	2	2	3	3	3
·23	1698	1702	1706	1710	1714	1718	1722	1726	1730	1734	0	1	1	2	2	2	3	3	4
·24	1738	1742	1746	1750	1754	1758	1762	1766	1770	1774	0	1	1	2	2	2	3	3	4
·25	1778	1782	1786	1791	1795	1799	1803	1807	1811	1816	0	1	1	2	2	2	3	3	4
·26	1820	1824	1828	1832	1837	1841	1845	1849	1854	1858	0	1	1	2	2	3	3	3	4
·27	1862	1866	1871	1875	1879	1884	1888	1892	1897	1901	0	1	1	2	2	3	3	3	4
·28	1905	1910	1914	1919	1923	1928	1932	1936	1941	1945	0	1	1	2	2	3	3	4	4
·29	1950	1954	1959	1963	1968	1972	1977	1982	1986	1991	0	1	1	2	2	3	3	4	4
·30	1995	2000	2004	2009	2014	2018	2023	2028	2032	2037	0	1	1	2	2	3	3	4	4
·31	2042	2046	2051	2056	2061	2065	2070	2075	2080	2084	0	1	1	2	2	3	3	4	4
·32	2089	2094	2099	2104	2109	2113	2118	2123	2128	2133	0	1	1	2	2	3	3	4	4
·33	2138	2143	2148	2153	2158	2163	2168	2173	2178	2183	0	1	1	2	2	3	3	4	4
·34	2188	2193	2198	2203	2208	2213	2218	2223	2228	2234	1	1	2	2	3	3	4	4	5
·35	2239	2244	2249	2254	2259	2265	2270	2275	2280	2286	1	1	2	2	3	3	4	4	5
·36	2291	2296	2301	2307	2312	2317	2323	2328	2333	2339	1	1	2	2	3	3	4	4	5
·37	2344	2350	2355	2360	2366	2371	2377	2382	2388	2393	1	1	2	2	3	3	4	4	5
·38	2399	2404	2410	2415	2421	2427	2432	2438	2443	2449	1	1	2	2	3	3	4	4	5
·39	2455	2460	2466	2472	2477	2483	2489	2495	2500	2506	1	1	2	2	3	3	4	5	5
·40	2512	2518	2523	2529	2535	2541	2547	2553	2559	2564	1	1	2	2	3	4	4	5	5
·41	2570	2576	2582	2588	2594	2600	2606	2612	2618	2624	1	1	2	2	3	4	4	5	5
·42	2630	2636	2642	2649	2655	2661	2667	2673	2679	2685	1	1	2	3	3	4	4	5	6
·43	2692	2698	2704	2710	2716	2723	2729	2735	2742	2748	1	1	2	3	3	4	4	5	6
·44	2754	2761	2767	2773	2780	2786	2793	2799	2805	2812	1	1	2	3	3	4	4	5	6
·45	2818	2825	2831	2838	2844	2851	2858	2864	2871	2877	1	1	2	3	3	4	5	5	6
·46	2884	2891	2897	2904	2911	2917	2924	2931	2938	2944	1	1	2	3	3	4	5	5	6
·47	2951	2958	2965	2972	2979	2985	2992	2999	3006	3013	1	1	2	3	3	4	5	5	6
·48	3020	3027	3034	3041	3048	3055	3062	3069	3076	3083	1	1	2	3	4	4	5	6	6
·49	3090	3097	3105	3112	3119	3126	3133	3141	3148	3155	1	1	2	3	4	4	5	6	6

ANTI-LOGARITHMS.

Log.	0	1	2	3	4	5	6	7	8	9	1	2	3	4	5	6	7	8	9
·50	3162	3170	3177	3184	3192	3199	3206	3214	3221	3228	1	1	2	3	4	4	5	6	7
·51	3236	3243	3251	3258	3266	3273	3281	3289	3296	3304	1	2	2	3	4	5	5	6	7
·52	3311	3319	3327	3334	3342	3350	3357	3365	3373	3381	1	2	2	3	4	5	5	6	7
·53	3388	3396	3404	3412	3420	3428	3436	3443	3451	3459	1	2	2	3	4	5	6	6	7
·54	3467	3475	3483	3491	3499	3508	3516	3524	3532	3540	1	2	2	3	4	5	6	6	7
·55	3548	3556	3565	3573	3581	3589	3597	3606	3614	3622	1	2	2	3	4	5	6	7	7
·56	3631	3639	3648	3656	3664	3673	3681	3690	3698	3707	1	2	3	3	4	5	6	7	8
·57	3715	3724	3733	3741	3750	3758	3767	3776	3784	3793	1	2	3	3	4	5	6	7	8
·58	3802	3811	3819	3828	3837	3846	3855	3864	3873	3882	1	2	3	4	4	5	6	7	8
·59	3890	3899	3908	3917	3926	3936	3945	3954	3963	3972	1	2	3	4	5	5	6	7	8
·60	3981	3990	3999	4009	4018	4027	4036	4046	4055	4064	1	2	3	4	5	6	6	7	8
·61	4074	4083	4093	4102	4111	4121	4130	4140	4150	4159	1	2	3	4	5	6	7	8	9
·62	4169	4178	4188	4198	4207	4217	4227	4236	4246	4256	1	2	3	4	5	6	7	8	9
·63	4266	4276	4285	4295	4305	4315	4325	4335	4345	4355	1	2	3	4	5	6	7	8	9
·64	4365	4375	4385	4395	4406	4416	4426	4436	4446	4457	1	2	3	4	5	6	7	8	9
·65	4467	4477	4487	4498	4508	4519	4529	4539	4550	4560	1	2	3	4	5	6	7	8	9
·66	4571	4581	4592	4603	4613	4624	4634	4645	4656	4667	1	2	3	4	5	6	7	9	10
·67	4677	4688	4699	4710	4721	4732	4742	4753	4764	4775	1	2	3	4	5	7	8	9	10
·68	4786	4797	4808	4819	4831	4842	4853	4864	4875	4887	1	2	3	4	6	7	8	9	10
·69	4898	4909	4920	4932	4943	4955	4966	4977	4989	5000	1	2	3	5	6	7	8	9	10
·70	5012	5023	5035	5047	5058	5070	5082	5093	5105	5117	1	2	4	5	6	7	8	9	11
·71	5129	5140	5152	5164	5176	5188	5200	5212	5224	5236	1	2	4	5	6	7	8	10	11
·72	5248	5260	5272	5284	5297	5309	5321	5333	5346	5358	1	2	4	5	6	7	9	10	11
·73	5370	5383	5395	5408	5420	5433	5445	5458	5470	5483	1	3	4	5	6	8	9	10	11
·74	5495	5508	5521	5534	5546	5559	5572	5585	5598	5610	1	3	4	5	6	8	9	10	12
·75	5623	5636	5649	5662	5675	5689	5702	5715	5728	5741	1	3	4	5	7	8	9	10	12
·76	5754	5768	5781	5794	5808	5821	5834	5848	5861	5875	1	3	4	5	7	8	9	11	12
·77	5888	5902	5916	5929	5943	5957	5970	5984	5998	6012	1	3	4	5	7	8	10	11	12
·78	6026	6039	6053	6067	6081	6095	6109	6124	6138	6152	1	3	4	6	7	8	10	11	12
·79	6166	6180	6194	6209	6223	6237	6252	6266	6281	6295	1	3	4	6	7	9	10	11	13
·80	6310	6324	6339	6353	6368	6383	6397	6412	6427	6442	1	3	4	6	7	9	10	12	13
·81	6457	6471	6486	6501	6516	6531	6546	6561	6577	6592	2	3	5	6	8	9	11	12	14
·82	6607	6622	6637	6653	6668	6683	6699	6714	6730	6745	2	3	5	6	8	9	11	12	14
·83	6761	6776	6792	6808	6823	6839	6855	6871	6887	6902	2	3	5	6	8	9	11	13	14
·84	6918	6934	6950	6966	6982	6998	7015	7031	7047	7063	2	3	5	6	8	10	11	13	15
·85	7079	7096	7112	7129	7145	7161	7178	7194	7211	7228	2	3	5	7	8	10	12	13	15
·86	7244	7261	7278	7295	7311	7328	7345	7362	7379	7396	2	3	5	7	8	10	12	13	15
·87	7413	7430	7447	7464	7482	7499	7516	7534	7551	7568	2	3	5	7	9	10	12	14	16
·88	7586	7603	7621	7638	7656	7674	7691	7709	7727	7745	2	4	5	7	9	11	12	14	16
·89	7762	7780	7798	7816	7834	7852	7870	7889	7907	7925	2	4	5	7	9	11	13	14	16
·90	7943	7962	7980	7998	8017	8035	8054	8072	8091	8110	2	4	6	7	9	11	13	15	17
·91	8128	8147	8166	8185	8204	8222	8241	8260	8279	8299	2	4	6	8	9	11	13	15	17
·92	8318	8337	8356	8375	8395	8414	8433	8453	8472	8492	2	4	6	8	10	12	14	15	17
·93	8511	8531	8551	8570	8590	8610	8630	8650	8670	8690	2	4	6	8	10	12	14	16	18
·94	8710	8730	8750	8770	8790	8810	8831	8851	8872	8892	2	4	6	8	10	12	14	16	18
·95	8913	8933	8954	8974	8995	9016	9036	9057	9078	9099	2	4	6	8	10	12	15	17	19
·96	9120	9141	9162	9183	9204	9226	9247	9268	9290	9311	2	4	6	8	11	13	15	17	19
·97	9333	9354	9376	9397	9419	9441	9462	9484	9506	9528	2	4	7	9	11	13	15	17	20
·98	9550	9572	9594	9616	9638	9661	9683	9705	9727	9750	2	4	7	9	11	13	16	18	20
·99	9772	9795	9817	9840	9863	9886	9908	9931	9954	9977	2	5	7	9	11	14	16	18	20

NATURAL SINES.

Angle	0'	6'	12'	18'	24'	30'	36'	42'	48'	54'	1'	2'	3'	4'	5'
0°	·0000	·0017	·0035	·0052	·0070	·0087	·0105	·0122	·0140	·0157	3	6	9	12	15
1°	·0175	·0192	·0209	·0227	·0244	·0262	·0279	·0297	·0314	·0332	3	6	9	12	15
2°	·0349	·0366	·0384	·0401	·0419	·0436	·0454	·0471	·0488	·0506	3	6	9	12	15
3°	·0523	·0541	·0558	·0576	·0593	·0610	·0628	·0645	·0663	·0680	3	6	9	12	15
4°	·0698	·0715	·0732	·0750	·0767	·0785	·0802	·0819	·0837	·0854	3	6	9	12	14
5°	·0872	·0889	·0906	·0924	·0941	·0958	·0976	·0993	·1011	·1028	3	6	9	12	14
6°	·1045	·1063	·1080	·1097	·1115	·1132	·1149	·1167	·1184	·1201	3	6	9	12	14
7°	·1219	·1236	·1253	·1271	·1288	·1305	·1323	·1340	·1357	·1374	3	6	9	12	14
8°	·1392	·1409	·1426	·1444	·1461	·1478	·1495	·1513	·1530	·1547	3	6	9	12	14
9°	·1564	·1582	·1599	·1616	·1633	·1650	·1668	·1685	·1702	·1719	3	6	9	12	14
10°	·1736	·1754	·1771	·1788	·1805	·1822	·1840	·1857	·1874	·1891	3	6	9	11	14
11°	·1908	·1925	·1942	·1959	·1977	·1994	·2011	·2028	·2045	·2062	3	6	9	11	14
12°	·2079	·2096	·2113	·2130	·2147	·2164	·2181	·2198	·2215	·2233	3	6	9	11	14
13°	·2250	·2267	·2284	·2300	·2317	·2334	·2351	·2368	·2385	·2402	3	6	8	11	14
14°	·2419	·2436	·2453	·2470	·2487	·2504	·2521	·2538	·2554	·2571	3	6	8	11	14
15°	·2588	·2605	·2622	·2639	·2656	·2672	·2689	·2706	·2723	·2740	3	6	8	11	14
16°	·2756	·2773	·2790	·2807	·2823	·2840	·2857	·2874	·2890	·2907	3	6	8	11	14
17°	·2924	·2940	·2957	·2974	·2990	·3007	·3024	·3040	·3057	·3074	3	6	8	11	14
18°	·3090	·3107	·3123	·3140	·3156	·3173	·3190	·3206	·3223	·3239	3	6	8	11	14
19°	·3256	·3272	·3289	·3305	·3322	·3338	·3355	·3371	·3387	·3404	3	5	8	11	14
20°	·3420	·3437	·3453	·3469	·3486	·3502	·3518	·3535	·3551	·3567	3	5	8	11	14
21°	·3584	·3600	·3616	·3633	·3649	·3665	·3681	·3697	·3714	·3730	3	5	8	11	14
22°	·3746	·3762	·3778	·3795	·3811	·3827	·3843	·3859	·3875	·3891	3	5	8	11	14
23°	·3907	·3923	·3939	·3955	·3971	·3987	·4003	·4019	·4035	·4051	3	5	8	11	14
24°	·4067	·4083	·4099	·4115	·4131	·4147	·4163	·4179	·4195	·4210	3	5	8	11	13
25°	·4226	·4242	·4258	·4274	·4289	·4305	·4321	·4337	·4352	·4368	3	5	8	11	13
26°	·4384	·4399	·4415	·4431	·4446	·4462	·4478	·4493	·4509	·4524	3	5	8	10	13
27°	·4540	·4555	·4571	·4586	·4602	·4617	·4633	·4648	·4664	·4679	3	5	8	10	13
28°	·4695	·4710	·4726	·4741	·4756	·4772	·4787	·4802	·4818	·4833	3	5	8	10	13
29°	·4848	·4863	·4879	·4894	·4909	·4924	·4939	·4955	·4970	·4985	3	5	8	10	13
30°	·5000	·5015	·5030	·5045	·5060	·5075	·5090	·5105	·5120	·5135	3	5	8	10	13
31°	·5150	·5165	·5180	·5195	·5210	·5225	·5240	·5255	·5270	·5284	2	5	7	10	12
32°	·5299	·5314	·5329	·5344	·5358	·5373	·5388	·5402	·5417	·5432	2	5	7	10	12
33°	·5446	·5461	·5476	·5490	·5505	·5519	·5534	·5548	·5563	·5577	2	5	7	10	12
34°	·5592	·5606	·5621	·5635	·5650	·5664	·5678	·5693	·5707	·5721	2	5	7	10	12
35°	·5736	·5750	·5764	·5779	·5793	·5807	·5821	·5835	·5850	·5864	2	5	7	9	12
36°	·5878	·5892	·5906	·5920	·5934	·5948	·5962	·5976	·5990	·6004	2	5	7	9	12
37°	·6018	·6032	·6046	·6060	·6074	·6088	·6101	·6115	·6129	·6143	2	5	7	9	12
38°	·6157	·6170	·6184	·6198	·6211	·6225	·6239	·6252	·6266	·6280	2	5	7	9	11
39°	·6293	·6307	·6320	·6334	·6347	·6361	·6374	·6388	·6401	·6414	2	4	7	9	11
40°	·6428	·6441	·6455	·6468	·6481	·6494	·6508	·6521	·6534	·6547	2	4	7	9	11
41°	·6561	·6574	·6587	·6600	·6613	·6626	·6639	·6652	·6665	·6678	2	4	7	9	11
42°	·6691	·6704	·6717	·6730	·6743	·6756	·6769	·6782	·6794	·6807	2	4	6	9	11
43°	·6820	·6833	·6845	·6858	·6871	·6884	·6896	·6909	·6921	·6934	2	4	6	8	11
44°	·6947	·6959	·6972	·6984	·6997	·7009	·7022	·7034	·7046	·7059	2	4	6	8	10

NATURAL SINES.

Angle	0′	6′	12′	18′	24′	30′	36′	42′	48′	54′	1′	2′	3′	4′	5′
45°	·7071	·7083	·7096	·7108	·7120	·7133	·7145	·7157	·7169	·7181	2	4	6	8	10
46°	·7193	·7206	·7218	·7230	·7242	·7254	·7266	·7278	·7290	·7302	2	4	6	8	10
47°	·7314	·7325	·7337	·7349	·7361	·7373	·7385	·7396	·7408	·7420	2	4	6	8	10
48°	·7431	·7443	·7455	·7466	·7478	·7490	·7501	·7513	·7524	·7536	2	4	6	8	10
49°	·7547	·7559	·7570	·7581	·7593	·7604	·7615	·7627	·7638	·7649	2	4	6	8	9
50°	·7660	·7672	·7683	·7694	·7705	·7716	·7727	·7738	·7749	·7760	2	4	6	7	9
51°	·7771	·7782	·7793	·7804	·7815	·7826	·7837	·7848	·7859	·7869	2	4	5	7	9
52°	·7880	·7891	·7902	·7912	·7923	·7934	·7944	·7955	·7965	·7976	2	4	5	7	9
53°	·7986	·7997	·8007	·8018	·8028	·8039	·8049	·8059	·8070	·8080	2	3	5	7	9
54°	·8090	·8100	·8111	·8121	·8131	·8141	·8151	·8161	·8171	·8181	2	3	5	7	8
55°	·8192	·8202	·8211	·8221	·8231	·8241	·8251	·8261	·8271	·8281	2	3	5	7	8
56°	·8290	·8300	·8310	·8320	·8329	·8339	·8348	·8358	·8368	·8377	2	3	5	6	8
57°	·8387	·8396	·8406	·8415	·8425	·8434	·8443	·8453	·8462	·8471	2	3	5	6	8
58°	·8480	·8490	·8499	·8508	·8517	·8526	·8536	·8545	·8554	·8563	2	3	5	6	8
59°	·8572	·8581	·8590	·8599	·8607	·8616	·8625	·8634	·8643	·8652	1	3	4	6	7
60°	·8660	·8669	·8678	·8686	·8695	·8704	·8712	·8721	·8729	·8738	1	3	4	6	7
61°	·8746	·8755	·8763	·8771	·8780	·8788	·8796	·8805	·8813	·8821	1	3	4	6	7
62°	·8829	·8838	·8846	·8854	·8862	·8870	·8878	·8886	·8894	·8902	1	3	4	5	7
63°	·8910	·8918	·8926	·8934	·8942	·8949	·8957	·8965	·8973	·8980	1	3	4	5	6
64°	·8988	·8996	·9003	·9011	·9018	·9026	·9033	·9041	·9048	·9056	1	3	4	5	6
65°	·9063	·9070	·9078	·9085	·9092	·9100	·9107	·9114	·9121	·9128	1	2	4	5	6
66°	·9135	·9143	·9150	·9157	·9164	·9171	·9178	·9184	·9191	·9198	1	2	3	5	6
67°	·9205	·9212	·9219	·9225	·9232	·9239	·9245	·9252	·9259	·9265	1	2	3	4	6
68°	·9272	·9278	·9285	·9291	·9298	·9304	·9311	·9317	·9323	·9330	1	2	3	4	5
69°	·9336	·9342	·9348	·9354	·9361	·9367	·9373	·9379	·9385	·9391	1	2	3	4	5
70°	·9397	·9403	·9409	·9415	·9421	·9426	·9432	·9438	·9444	·9449	1	2	3	4	5
71°	·9455	·9461	·9466	·9472	·9478	·9483	·9489	·9494	·9500	·9505	1	2	3	4	5
72°	·9511	·9516	·9521	·9527	·9532	·9537	·9542	·9548	·9553	·9558	1	2	3	3	4
73°	·9563	·9568	·9573	·9578	·9583	·9588	·9593	·9598	·9603	·9608	1	2	2	3	4
74°	·9613	·9617	·9622	·9627	·9632	·9636	·9641	·9646	·9650	·9655	1	2	2	3	4
75°	·9659	·9664	·9668	·9673	·9677	·9681	·9686	·9690	·9694	·9699	1	1	2	3	4
76°	·9703	·9707	·9711	·9715	·9720	·9724	·9728	·9732	·9736	·9740	1	1	2	3	3
77°	·9744	·9748	·9751	·9755	·9759	·9763	·9767	·9770	·9774	·9778	1	1	2	3	3
78°	·9781	·9785	·9789	·9792	·9796	·9799	·9803	·9806	·9810	·9813	1	1	2	2	3
79°	·9816	·9820	·9823	·9826	·9829	·9833	·9836	·9839	·9842	·9845	1	1	2	2	3
80°	·9848	·9851	·9854	·9857	·9860	·9863	·9866	·9869	·9871	·9874	0	1	1	2	2
81°	·9877	·9880	·9882	·9885	·9888	·9890	·9893	·9895	·9898	·9900	0	1	1	2	2
82°	·9903	·9905	·9907	·9910	·9912	·9914	·9917	·9919	·9921	·9923	0	1	1	2	2
83°	·9925	·9928	·9930	·9932	·9934	·9936	·9938	·9940	·9942	·9943	0	1	1	1	2
84°	·9945	·9947	·9949	·9951	·9952	·9954	·9956	·9957	·9959	·9960	0	1	1	1	1
85°	·9962	·9963	·9965	·9966	·9968	·9969	·9971	·9972	·9973	·9974	0	0	1	1	1
86°	·9976	·9977	·9978	·9979	·9980	·9981	·9982	·9983	·9984	·9985	0	0	1	1	1
87°	·9986	·9987	·9988	·9989	·9990	·9990	·9991	·9992	·9993	·9993	0	0	0	1	1
88°	·9994	·9995	·9995	·9996	·9996	·9997	·9997	·9997	·9998	·9998	0	0	0	0	0
89°	·9998	·9999	·9999	·9999	·9999	1·000	1·000	1·000	1·000	1·000	0	0	0	0	0

Angle	0′	6′	12′	18′	24′	30′	36′	42′	48′	54′	1′	2′	3′	4′	5′
0°	1·0000	1·000	1·000	1·000	1·000	1·000	·9999	·9999	·9999	·9999	0	0	0	0	0
1°	·9998	·9998	·9998	·9997	·9997	·9997	·9996	·9996	·9995	·9995	0	0	0	0	0
2°	·9994	·9993	·9993	·9992	·9991	·9990	·9990	·9989	·9988	·9987	0	0	0	0	0
3°	·9986	·9985	·9984	·9983	·9982	·9981	·9980	·9979	·9978	·9977	0	0	1	1	1
4°	·9976	·9974	·9973	·9972	·9971	·9969	·9968	·9966	·9965	·9963	0	0	1	1	1
5°	·9962	·9960	·9959	·9957	·9956	·9954	·9952	·9951	·9949	·9947	0	1	1	1	1
6°	·9945	·9943	·9942	·9940	·9938	·9936	·9934	·9932	·9930	·9928	0	1	1	1	2
7°	·9925	·9923	·9921	·9919	·9917	·9914	·9912	·9910	·9907	·9905	0	1	1	2	2
8°	·9903	·9900	·9898	·9895	·9893	·9890	·9888	·9885	·9882	·9880	0	1	1	2	2
9°	·9877	·9874	·9871	·9869	·9866	·9863	·9860	·9857	·9854	·9851	0	1	1	2	2
10°	·9848	·9845	·9842	·9839	·9836	·9833	·9829	·9826	·9823	·9820	1	1	2	2	3
11°	·9816	·9813	·9810	·9806	·9803	·9799	·9796	·9792	·9789	·9785	1	1	2	2	3
12°	·9781	·9778	·9774	·9770	·9767	·9763	·9759	·9755	·9751	·9748	1	1	2	3	3
13°	·9744	·9740	·9736	·9732	·9728	·9724	·9720	·9715	·9711	·9707	1	1	2	3	3
14°	·9703	·9699	·9694	·9690	·9686	·9681	·9677	·9673	·9668	·9664	1	1	2	3	4
15°	·9659	·9655	·9650	·9646	·9641	·9636	·9632	·9627	·9622	·9617	1	2	2	3	4
16°	·9613	·9608	·9603	·9598	·9593	·9588	·9583	·9578	·9573	·9568	1	2	2	3	4
17°	·9563	·9558	·9553	·9548	·9542	·9537	·9532	·9527	·9521	·9516	1	2	3	4	4
18°	·9511	·9505	·9500	·9494	·9489	·9483	·9478	·9472	·9466	·9461	1	2	3	4	5
19°	·9455	·9449	·9444	·9438	·9432	·9426	·9421	·9415	·9409	·9403	1	2	3	4	5
20°	·9397	·9391	·9385	·9379	·9373	·9367	·9361	·9354	·9348	·9342	1	2	3	4	5
21°	·9336	·9330	·9323	·9317	·9311	·9304	·9298	·9291	·9285	·9278	1	2	3	4	5
22°	·9272	·9265	·9259	·9252	·9245	·9239	·9232	·9225	·9219	·9212	1	2	3	4	6
23°	·9205	·9198	·9191	·9184	·9178	·9171	·9164	·9157	·9150	·9143	1	2	3	5	6
24°	·9135	·9128	·9121	·9114	·9107	·9100	·9092	·9085	·9078	·9070	1	2	4	5	6
25°	·9063	·9056	·9048	·9041	·9033	·9026	·9018	·9011	·9003	·8996	1	3	4	5	6
26°	·8988	·8980	·8973	·8965	·8957	·8949	·8942	·8934	·8926	·8918	1	3	4	5	6
27°	·8910	·8902	·8894	·8886	·8878	·8870	·8862	·8854	·8846	·8838	1	3	4	5	7
28°	·8829	·8821	·8813	·8805	·8796	·8788	·8780	·8771	·8763	·8755	1	3	4	6	7
29°	·8746	·8738	·8729	·8721	·8712	·8704	·8695	·8686	·8678	·8669	1	3	4	6	7
30°	·8660	·8652	·8643	·8634	·8625	·8616	·8607	·8599	·8590	·8581	1	3	4	6	7
31°	·8572	·8563	·8554	·8545	·8536	·8526	·8517	·8508	·8499	·8490	2	3	5	6	8
32°	·8480	·8471	·8462	·8453	·8443	·8434	·8425	·8415	·8406	·8396	2	3	5	6	8
33°	·8387	·8377	·8368	·8358	·8348	·8339	·8329	·8320	·8310	·8300	2	3	5	6	8
34°	·8290	·8281	·8271	·8261	·8251	·8241	·8231	·8221	·8211	·8202	2	3	5	7	8
35°	·8192	·8181	·8171	·8161	·8151	·8141	·8131	·8121	·8111	·8100	2	3	5	7	8
36°	·8090	·8080	·8070	·8059	·8049	·8039	·8028	·8018	·8007	·7997	2	3	5	7	9
37°	·7986	·7976	·7965	·7955	·7944	·7934	·7923	·7912	·7902	·7891	2	4	5	7	9
38°	·7880	·7869	·7859	·7848	·7837	·7826	·7815	·7804	·7793	·7782	2	4	5	7	9
39°	·7771	·7760	·7749	·7738	·7727	·7716	·7705	·7694	·7683	·7672	2	4	6	7	9
40°	·7660	·7649	·7638	·7627	·7615	·7604	·7593	·7581	·7570	·7559	2	4	6	8	9
41°	·7547	·7536	·7524	·7513	·7501	·7490	·7478	·7466	·7455	·7443	2	4	6	8	10
42°	·7431	·7420	·7408	·7396	·7385	·7373	·7361	·7349	·7337	·7325	2	4	6	8	10
43°	·7314	·7302	·7290	·7278	·7266	·7254	·7242	·7230	·7218	·7206	2	4	6	8	10
44°	·7193	·7181	·7169	·7157	·7145	·7133	·7120	·7108	·7096	·7083	2	4	6	8	10

Angle	0'	6'	12'	18'	24'	30'	36'	42'	48'	54'	1'	2'	3'	4'	5'
45°	·7071	·7059	·7046	·7034	·7022	·7009	·6997	·6984	·6972	·6959	2	4	6	8	10
46°	·6947	·6934	·6921	·6909	·6896	·6884	·6871	·6858	·6845	·6833	2	4	6	8	11
47°	·6820	·6807	·6794	·6782	·6769	·6756	·6743	·6730	·6717	·6704	2	4	6	9	11
48°	·6691	·6678	·6665	·6652	·6639	·6626	·6613	·6600	·6587	·6574	2	4	7	9	11
49°	·6561	·6547	·6534	·6521	·6508	·6494	·6481	·6468	·6455	·6441	2	4	7	9	11
50°	·6428	·6414	·6401	·6388	·6374	·6361	·6347	·6334	·6320	·6307	2	4	7	9	11
51°	·6293	·6280	·6266	·6252	·6239	·6225	·6211	·6198	·6184	·6170	2	5	7	9	11
52°	·6157	·6143	·6129	·6115	·6101	·6088	·6074	·6060	·6046	·6032	2	5	7	9	12
53°	·6018	·6004	·5990	·5976	·5962	·5948	·5934	·5920	·5906	·5892	2	5	7	9	12
54°	·5878	·5864	·5850	·5835	·5821	·5807	·5793	·5779	·5764	·5750	2	5	7	9	12
55°	·5736	·5721	·5707	·5693	·5678	·5664	·5650	·5635	·5621	·5606	2	5	7	10	12
56°	·5592	·5577	·5563	·5548	·5534	·5519	·5505	·5490	·5476	·5461	2	5	7	10	12
57°	·5446	·5432	·5417	·5402	·5388	·5373	·5358	·5344	·5329	·5314	2	5	7	10	12
58°	·5299	·5284	·5270	·5255	·5240	·5225	·5210	·5195	·5180	·5165	2	5	7	10	12
59°	·5150	·5135	·5120	·5105	·5090	·5075	·5060	·5045	·5030	·5015	3	5	8	10	13
60°	·5000	·4985	·4970	·4955	·4939	·4924	·4909	·4894	·4879	·4863	3	5	8	10	13
61°	·4848	·4833	·4818	·4802	·4787	·4772	·4756	·4741	·4726	·4710	3	5	8	10	13
62°	·4695	·4679	·4664	·4648	·4633	·4617	·4602	·4586	·4571	·4555	3	5	8	10	13
63°	·4540	·4524	·4509	·4493	·4478	·4462	·4446	·4431	·4415	·4399	3	5	8	10	13
64°	·4384	·4368	·4352	·4337	·4321	·4305	·4289	·4274	·4258	·4242	3	5	8	11	13
65°	·4226	·4210	·4195	·4179	·4163	·4147	·4131	·4115	·4099	·4083	3	5	8	11	13
66°	·4067	·4051	·4035	·4019	·4003	·3987	·3971	·3955	·3939	·3923	3	5	8	11	13
67°	·3907	·3891	·3875	·3859	·3843	·3827	·3811	·3795	·3778	·3762	3	5	8	11	13
68°	·3746	·3730	·3714	·3697	·3681	·3665	·3649	·3633	·3616	·3600	3	5	8	11	14
69°	·3584	·3567	·3551	·3535	·3518	·3502	·3486	·3469	·3453	·3437	3	5	8	11	14
70°	·3420	·3404	·3387	·3371	·3355	·3338	·3322	·3305	·3289	·3272	3	5	8	11	14
71°	·3256	·3239	·3223	·3206	·3190	·3173	·3156	·3140	·3123	·3107	3	6	8	11	14
72°	·3090	·3074	·3057	·3040	·3024	·3007	·2990	·2974	·2957	·2940	3	6	8	11	14
73°	·2924	·2907	·2890	·2874	·2857	·2840	·2823	·2807	·2790	·2773	3	6	8	11	14
74°	·2756	·2740	·2723	·2706	·2689	·2672	·2656	·2639	·2622	·2605	3	6	8	11	14
75°	·2588	·2571	·2554	·2538	·2521	·2504	·2487	·2470	·2453	·2436	3	6	8	11	14
76°	·2419	·2402	·2385	·2368	·2351	·2334	·2317	·2300	·2284	·2267	3	6	8	11	14
77°	·2250	·2233	·2215	·2198	·2181	·2164	·2147	·2130	·2113	·2096	3	6	9	11	14
78°	·2079	·2062	·2045	·2028	·2011	·1994	·1977	·1959	·1942	·1925	3	6	9	11	14
79°	·1908	·1891	·1874	·1857	·1840	·1822	·1805	·1788	·1771	·1754	3	6	9	11	14
80°	·1736	·1719	·1702	·1685	·1668	·1650	·1633	·1616	·1599	·1582	3	6	9	11	14
81°	·1564	·1547	·1530	·1513	·1495	·1478	·1461	·1444	·1426	·1409	3	6	9	12	14
82°	·1392	·1374	·1357	·1340	·1323	·1305	·1288	·1271	·1253	·1236	3	6	9	12	14
83°	·1219	·1201	·1184	·1167	·1149	·1132	·1115	·1097	·1080	·1063	3	6	9	12	14
84°	·1045	·1028	·1011	·0993	·0976	·0958	·0941	·0924	·0906	·0889	3	6	9	12	14
85°	·0872	·0854	·0837	·0819	·0802	·0785	·0767	·0750	·0732	·0715	3	6	9	12	14
86°	·0698	·0680	·0663	·0645	·0628	·0610	·0593	·0576	·0558	·0541	3	6	9	12	15
87°	·0523	·0505	·0488	·0471	·0454	·0436	·0419	·0401	·0384	·0366	3	6	9	12	15
88°	·0349	·0332	·0314	·0297	·0279	·0262	·0244	·0227	·0209	·0192	3	6	9	12	15
89°	·0175	·0157	·0140	·0122	·0105	·0087	·0070	·0052	·0035	·0017	3	6	9	12	15

NATURAL TANGENTS.

Angle	0'	6'	12'	18'	24'	30'	36'	42'	48'	54'	1'	2'	3'	4'	5'
0°	0·0000	·0017	·0035	·0052	·0070	·0087	·0105	·0122	·0140	·0157	3	6	9	12	15
1°	0·0175	·0192	·0209	·0227	·0244	·0262	·0279	·0297	·0314	·0332	3	6	9	12	15
2°	0·0349	·0367	·0384	·0402	·0419	·0437	·0454	·0472	·0489	·0507	3	6	9	12	15
3°	0·0524	·0542	·0559	·0577	·0594	·0612	·0629	·0647	·0664	·0682	3	6	9	12	15
4°	0·0699	·0717	·0734	·0752	·0769	·0787	·0805	·0822	·0840	·0857	3	6	9	12	15
5°	0·0875	·0892	·0910	·0928	·0945	·0963	·0981	·0998	·1016	·1033	3	6	9	12	15
6°	0·1051	·1069	·1086	·1104	·1122	·1139	·1157	·1175	·1192	·1210	3	6	9	12	15
7°	0·1228	·1246	·1263	·1281	·1299	·1317	·1334	·1352	·1370	·1388	3	6	9	12	15
8°	0·1405	·1423	·1441	·1459	·1477	·1495	·1512	·1530	·1548	·1566	3	6	9	12	15
9°	0·1584	·1602	·1620	·1638	·1655	·1673	·1691	·1709	·1727	·1745	3	6	9	12	15
10°	0·1763	·1781	·1799	·1817	·1835	·1853	·1871	·1890	·1908	·1926	3	6	9	12	15
11°	0·1944	·1962	·1980	·1998	·2016	·2035	·2053	·2071	·2089	·2107	3	6	9	12	15
12°	0·2126	·2144	·2162	·2180	·2199	·2217	·2235	·2254	·2272	·2290	3	6	9	12	15
13°	0·2309	·2327	·2345	·2364	·2382	·2401	·2419	·2438	·2456	·2475	3	6	9	12	15
14°	0·2493	·2512	·2530	·2549	·2568	·2586	·2605	·2623	·2642	·2661	3	6	9	12	16
15°	0·2679	·2698	·2717	·2736	·2754	·2773	·2792	·2811	·2830	·2849	3	6	9	13	16
16°	0·2867	·2886	·2905	·2924	·2943	·2962	·2981	·3000	·3019	·3038	3	6	9	13	16
17°	0·3057	·3076	·3096	·3115	·3134	·3153	·3172	·3191	·3211	·3230	3	6	10	13	16
18°	0·3249	·3269	·3288	·3307	·3327	·3346	·3365	·3385	·3404	·3424	3	6	10	13	16
19°	0·3443	·3463	·3482	·3502	·3522	·3541	·3561	·3581	·3600	·3620	3	7	10	13	16
20°	0·3640	·3659	·3679	·3699	·3719	·3739	·3759	·3779	·3799	·3819	3	7	10	13	17
21°	0·3839	·3859	·3879	·3899	·3919	·3939	·3959	·3979	·4000	·4020	3	7	10	13	17
22°	0·4040	·4061	·4081	·4101	·4122	·4142	·4163	·4183	·4204	·4224	3	7	10	14	17
23°	0·4245	·4265	·4286	·4307	·4327	·4348	·4369	·4390	·4411	·4431	3	7	10	14	17
24°	0·4452	·4473	·4494	·4515	·4536	·4557	·4578	·4599	·4621	·4642	4	7	11	14	18
25°	0·4663	·4684	·4706	·4727	·4748	·4770	·4791	·4813	·4834	·4856	4	7	11	14	18
26°	0·4877	·4899	·4921	·4942	·4964	·4986	·5008	·5029	·5051	·5073	4	7	11	15	18
27°	0·5095	·5117	·5139	·5161	·5184	·5206	·5228	·5250	·5272	·5295	4	7	11	15	18
28°	0·5317	·5340	·5362	·5384	·5407	·5430	·5452	·5475	·5498	·5520	4	8	11	15	19
29°	0·5543	·5566	·5589	·5612	·5635	·5658	·5681	·5704	·5727	·5750	4	8	12	15	19
30°	0·5774	·5797	·5820	·5844	·5867	·5890	·5914	·5938	·5961	·5985	4	8	12	16	20
31°	0·6009	·6032	·6056	·6080	·6104	·6128	·6152	·6176	·6200	·6224	4	8	12	16	20
32°	0·6249	·6273	·6297	·6322	·6346	·6371	·6395	·6420	·6445	·6469	4	8	12	16	20
33°	0·6494	·6519	·6544	·6569	·6594	·6619	·6644	·6669	·6694	·6720	4	8	13	17	21
34°	0·6745	·6771	·6796	·6822	·6847	·6873	·6899	·6924	·6950	·6976	4	9	13	17	21
35°	0·7002	·7028	·7054	·7080	·7107	·7133	·7159	·7186	·7212	·7239	4	9	13	18	22
36°	0·7265	·7292	·7319	·7346	·7373	·7400	·7427	·7454	·7481	·7508	5	9	14	18	23
37°	0·7536	·7563	·7590	·7618	·7646	·7673	·7701	·7729	·7757	·7785	5	9	14	18	23
38°	0·7813	·7841	·7869	·7898	·7926	·7954	·7983	·8012	·8040	·8069	5	9	14	19	24
39°	0·8098	·8127	·8156	·8185	·8214	·8243	·8273	·8302	·8332	·8361	5	10	15	20	24
40°	0·8391	·8421	·8451	·8481	·8511	·8541	·8571	·8601	·8632	·8662	5	10	15	20	25
41°	0·8693	·8724	·8754	·8785	·8816	·8847	·8878	·8910	·8941	·8972	5	10	16	21	26
42°	0·9004	·9036	·9067	·9099	·9131	·9163	·9195	·9228	·9260	·9293	5	11	16	21	27
43°	0·9325	·9358	·9391	·9424	·9457	·9490	·9523	·9556	·9590	·9623	6	11	17	22	28
44°	0·9657	·9691	·9725	·9759	·9793	·9827	·9861	·9896	·9930	·9965	6	11	17	23	29

NATURAL TANGENTS.

Angle	0′	6′	12′	18′	24′	30′	36′	42′	48′	54′	1′	2′	3′	4′	5′
45°	1·0000	1·0035	1·0070	1·0105	1·0141	1·0176	1·0212	1·0247	1·0283	1·0319	6	12	18	24	30
46°	1·0355	1·0392	1·0428	1·0464	1·0501	1·0538	1·0575	1·0612	1·0649	1·0686	6	12	18	25	31
47°	1·0724	1·0761	1·0799	1·0837	1·0875	1·0913	1·0951	1·0990	1·1028	1·1067	6	13	19	25	32
48°	1·1106	1·1145	1·1184	1·1224	1·1263	1·1303	1·1343	1·1383	1·1423	1·1463	7	13	20	26	33
49°	1·1504	1·1544	1·1585	1·1626	1·1667	1·1708	1·1750	1·1792	1·1833	1·1875	7	14	21	28	34
50°	1·1918	1·1960	1·2002	1·2045	1·2088	1·2131	1·2174	1·2218	1·2261	1·2305	7	14	22	29	36
51°	1·2349	1·2393	1·2437	1·2482	1·2527	1·2572	1·2617	1·2662	1·2708	1·2753	8	15	23	30	38
52°	1·2799	1·2846	1·2892	1·2938	1·2985	1·3032	1·3079	1·3127	1·3175	1·3222	8	16	24	31	39
53°	1·3270	1·3319	1·3367	1·3416	1·3465	1·3514	1·3564	1·3613	1·3663	1·3713	8	16	25	33	41
54°	1·3764	1·3814	1·3865	1·3916	1·3968	1·4019	1·4071	1·4124	1·4176	1·4229	9	17	26	34	43
55°	1·4281	1·4335	1·4388	1·4442	1·4496	1·4550	1·4605	1·4659	1·4715	1·4770	9	18	27	36	45
56°	1·4826	1·4882	1·4938	1·4994	1·5051	1·5108	1·5166	1·5224	1·5282	1·5340	10	19	29	38	48
57°	1·5399	1·5458	1·5517	1·5577	1·5637	1·5697	1·5757	1·5818	1·5880	1·5941	10	20	30	40	50
58°	1·6003	1·6066	1·6128	1·6191	1·6255	1·6319	1·6383	1·6447	1·6512	1·6577	11	21	32	43	53
59°	1·6643	1·6709	1·6775	1·6842	1·6909	1·6977	1·7045	1·7113	1·7182	1·7251	11	23	34	45	56
60°	1·7321	1·7391	1·7461	1·7532	1·7603	1·7675	1·7747	1·7820	1·7893	1·7966	12	24	36	48	60
61°	1·8040	1·8115	1·8190	1·8265	1·8341	1·8418	1·8495	1·8572	1·8650	1·8728	13	26	38	51	64
62°	1·8807	1·8887	1·8967	1·9047	1·9128	1·9210	1·9292	1·9375	1·9458	1·9542	14	27	41	55	68
63°	1·9626	1·9711	1·9797	1·9883	1·9970	2·0057	2·0145	2·0233	2·0323	2·0413	15	29	44	58	73
64°	2·0503	2·0594	2·0686	2·0778	2·0872	2·0965	2·1060	2·1155	2·1251	2·1348	16	31	47	63	78
65°	2·1445	2·1543	2·1642	2·1742	2·1842	2·1943	2·2045	2·2148	2·2251	2·2355	17	34	51	68	85
66°	2·2460	2·2566	2·2673	2·2781	2·2889	2·2998	2·3109	2·3220	2·3332	2·3445	18	37	55	73	92
67°	2·3559	2·3673	2·3789	2·3906	2·4023	2·4142	2·4262	2·4383	2·4504	2·4627	20	40	60	79	99
68°	2·4751	2·4876	2·5002	2·5129	2·5257	2·5386	2·5517	2·5649	2·5782	2·5916	22	43	65	87	108
69°	2·6051	2·6187	2·6325	2·6464	2·6605	2·6746	2·6889	2·7034	2·7179	2·7326	24	47	71	95	119
70°	2·7475	2·7625	2·7776	2·7929	2·8083	2·8239	2·8397	2·8556	2·8716	2·8878	26	52	78	104	130
71°	2·9042	2·9208	2·9375	2·9544	2·9714	2·9887	3·0061	3·0237	3·0415	3·0595	29	58	87	116	144
72°	3·0777	3·0961	3·1146	3·1334	3·1524	3·1716	3·1910	3·2106	3·2305	3·2506	32	64	96	129	161
73°	3·2709	3·2914	3·3122	3·3332	3·3544	3·3759	3·3977	3·4197	3·4420	3·4646	36	72	108	144	180
74°	3·4874	3·5105	3·5339	3·5576	3·5816	3·6059	3·6305	3·6554	3·6806	3·7062	41	81	122	163	204
75°	3·7321	3·7583	3·7848	3·8118	3·8391	3·8667	3·8947	3·9232	3·9520	3·9812					
76°	4·0108	4·0408	4·0713	4·1022	4·1335	4·1653	4·1976	4·2303	4·2635	4·2972					
77°	4·3315	4·3662	4·4015	4·4374	4·4737	4·5107	4·5483	4·5864	4·6252	4·6646					
78°	4·7046	4·7453	4·7867	4·8288	4·8716	4·9152	4·9594	5·0045	5·0504	5·0970					
79°	5·1446	5·1929	5·2422	5·2924	5·3435	5·3955	5·4486	5·5026	5·5578	5·6140					
80°	5·6713	5·7297	5·7894	5·8502	5·9124	5·9758	6·0405	6·1066	6·1742	6·2432					
81°	6·3138	6·3859	6·4596	6·5350	6·6122	6·6912	6·7720	6·8548	6·9395	7·0264	Mean differences not sufficiently accurate.				
82°	7·1154	7·2066	7·3002	7·3962	7·4947	7·5958	7·6996	7·8062	7·9158	8·0285					
83°	8·1443	8·2636	8·3863	8·5126	8·6427	8·7769	8·9152	9·0579	9·2052	9·3572					
84°	9·5144	9·6768	9·8448	10·019	10·199	10·385	10·579	10·780	10·988	11·205					
85°	11·430	11·664	11·909	12·163	12·429	12·706	12·996	13·300	13·617	13·951					
86°	14·301	14·669	15·056	15·464	15·895	16·350	16·832	17·343	17·886	18·464					
87°	19·081	19·740	20·446	21·205	22·022	22·904	23·859	24·898	26·031	27·271					
88°	28·636	30·145	31·821	33·694	35·801	38·188	40·917	44·066	47·740	52·081					
89°	57·290	63·657	71·615	81·847	95·489	114·59	143·24	190·98	286·48	572·96					

EXERCISE 1. Page 29

1. A = 1·29 lb. ; B = 4·83 lb.
2. Tie = 3 tons ; Jib = 5·19 tons.
3. Y = 288·7 lb. ; X = 577·4 lb.
4. 17·32 lb.
5. P = 133·5 lb. ; Q = 115·4 lb.
6. Pull = 26·6 lb. ; Reaction = 34·2 lb. ; Additional load 62·8 lb
7. 2·2 tons ; 2·68 tons.
8. 38·5 lb. in direction 66° 8′ north of west.
9. (a) 193·2 lb. along the canal ; 51·7 lb. towards the bank.
   (b) 329 lb. along the canal ; 11·7 lb. towards the opposite bank.
10. 231·5 tons ; 27° 19′ north of east.
11. 17·9 lb. ; 36° 48′ north of east.
12. Jib 21·9 tons ; Tie 15·45 tons.
13. Jib 4·06 tons ; Tie 2·19 tons.
14. 190 tons ; Max. thrust 592 tons.
15. 60° to the vertical.
16. 21·3 lb. ; 27·1 lb. (in 4 ft. cord).
17. Tension in cord 4·62 oz. ; Horizontal force = 2·31 oz.
18. 2·84 lb. ; 3·79 lb. (in 4 ft. rope).
19. 2330 lb. ; 167 lb. ft.
20. 5 tons in 2nd member ; 8·66 tons in 3rd member ; both compressive.
21. 9·88 lb. towards O, between OA and OB ; 41° 41′ to OA.
22. (a) 4·63 lb. ; (b) 4 lb.
23. 6·7 lb. in the 25 in. string ; 10·4 lb. in the 15 in. string.
24. 0·654 tons in each.
25. X = 16·9 lb ; Reaction = 36·25 lb.
26. (a) No ; (b) Magnitude increased to 3·56 lb., direction altered to 7° 36′ west of south.
27. 11·55 lb. ; 10·35 lb.
28. 1·622 cwt.
29. 11,123 lb. ; Pull in connection rod 11,300 lb. ; Reaction 1927 lb.
30. 64·5 lb. ; 18° 24′ east of north ; Vertical comp. 61·25 lb. ; Horizontal comp. 21·2 lb.

EXERCISE 2. Page 45

1. R_1 = 3·2 tons ; R_2 = 3·8 tons.
2. R_1 = $3\frac{3}{4}$ tons ; R_2 = $3\frac{3}{4}$ tons.
3. W = $3\frac{3}{4}$ tons ; A = $5\frac{3}{4}$ tons.
4. 16 ft. from A.
5. 4·06 lb.
6. 10·8 lb.

7. 2·83 lb.
8. 1800 lb.
9. (a) R.H. support 9·94 tons ; L.H. support 7·06 tons.
    (b) R.H. support 12·43 tons ; L.H. support 4·57 tons.
10. 8·4 in. from the weight.
11. C = 105 lb. ; D = 195 lb.
12. 944 lb.
13. 115·4 lb.
14. 2 lb.
15. 28·4 lb. ; 28·6 lb.
16. 50 lb.
17. L.H. support 380 lb. ; R.H. support 492 lb.
18. Support near A $76\frac{2}{3}$ lb. ; near B $23\frac{1}{3}$ lb.
19. A = 29 lb. ; B = 24 lb.
20. L.H. support 23·8 lb. ; R.H. support 26·2 lb.
21. Readings should be A = 4·5 lb., B = 2·5 lb.
22. P = 42·4 lb. ; Reaction 46·9 lb. at 25° 12′ to horizontal.
23. R.H. support 3906 lb. ; L.H. support 3234 lb.
24. $2883\frac{1}{3}$ lb. ; $4376\frac{2}{3}$ lb.
25. F = $23\frac{1}{3}$ lb. ; Force at fulcrum $36\frac{2}{3}$ lb.

EXERCISE 3.   Page 55

1. 10,130 lb. per sq. in. ; 0·00338. in.
2. 2100 lb. per sq. in. ; 0·0042 in.
3. 18,100 lb. per sq. in. ; 0·000775 ; 23·4 × 10⁶ lb. per sq. in.
4. 5060 lb. per sq. in.
5. 3060 lb. per sq. in.
6. 176 lb. ; 0·192 in.
7. 1·45 in. ; 0·048 in.
8. 946 lb. per sq. in ; 2130 lb. per sq. in. ; 0·000168 in.
9. 58 tons ; 4·6 tons per sq. in.
10. 0·0125 in.
11. 0·192 in.
12. 10·58 lb. ; 0·432 in. ; 42·32 lb. ; 0·108 in.
13. 1·625 tons per sq. in. ; 4·5 tons per sq. in. ; 0·0025 in.
14. 13,000 tons per sq. in.
15. 14,100 lb. per sq. in. ; 0·000481.
16. 11,900 tons per sq. in.
17. $3\frac{3}{4}$ in. ; $5\frac{1}{16}$ in.
18. 0·1344 in.
19. 1·238 in.
20. 16,000 lb. per sq. in. ; 0·000625 ; 25·6 × 10⁶ lb. per sq. in.
21. 11,320 lb.

EXERCISE 4. Page 71

1. 6·4 h.p. ; 66 h.p.
2. 41·66 m.p.h.
3. 143,360 ft. lb. ; 1280 ft. lb.
4. 640 h.p.
5. 2·02 h.p. ; 2·88 h.p.
6. 16,400 ft. lb.
7. 0·273 h.p.
8. 6·54 h.p.
9. 15·6 lb. ; 468 ft. lb.
10. 216,000 ft. lb. ; 9·6 h.p.
11. 1,125,000 ft. lb ; 786 h.p.
12. 262·5 ft. tons ; 23·8 h.p.
13. 687·5 ft. per min. ; 7·81 m.p.h.
14. 3920 ft. lb. ; 98 strokes.
15. 2640 ft. lb. ; 576 ft. lb.
16. 13,200 ft. lb.
17. 558 lb. ; 39,060 ft. lb.
18. 27·2 h.p. ; 0·127 pence.
19. 6336 cub. ft. per hour.
20. 0·0025 h.p.
21. 101,250 ft. lb. ; 20·45 h.p.
22. 1120 lb. pull ; 6625 lb. thrust ; 10·18 h.p.
23. 2·036 min.
24. 40,000 ft. tons ; 1810 h.p.
25. 4·072 min.
26. 33,600 ft. lb. ; 2·036 h.p.
27. 0·289 h.p.
28. 1200 ft. lb.

EXERCISE 5. Page 79

1. 43¾ lb. ; 57·2 lb.
2. 1674 lb.
3. 0·387.
4. 120 lb. ; 30,240 ft. lb. ; 0·915 h.p.
5. 0·25 ; 0·48 h.p.
6. 0·310 ; 7·29 lb.
7. 450 ft. tons ; 6·11 h.p.
8. 24 lb. ; 24 ft. lb.
9. 13½ lb.
10. 1,558·8 ft. lb. ; 0·4.

EXERCISE 6. Page 107

1. 240 ft. lb. ; 10 ft. ; 300 ft. lb. ; 80% ; 24 lb.
2. 300 ft. lb. ; 40 ft. ; 480 ft. lb. ; 62½% ; 7½ lb.

3. 30 lb. ; 60% ; 40 lb.
4. 12 lb. ; 75% ; 15 lb.
5. 226 ; 55%.
6. V.R. $3\frac{1}{2}$; Ideal 32 lb. ; Actual 40 lb.
7. 47·8%.
8. 180 lb.
9. 12·5%.
10. 375 lb.
11. $13\frac{1}{8}$ r.p.m.
12. 120 ; Ideal $37\frac{1}{4}$ lb. ; Actual 49·77 lb.
13. V.R. 28 ; M.A. 25 ; Efficiency 89·4%.
14. 86·1 r.p.m. ; 80 lb.
15. V.R. 28 ; 126 ft.
16. 512 lb. ; V.R. 16 ; M.A. 12·8.
17. 227 ft. min.
18. (a) 480 r.p.m. ; (b) 257·14 r.p.m.
19. 300 r.p.m. ; 182 r.p.m. ; 97·7 r.p.m. ; 59·2 r.p.m.
20. 61 lb.
21. 32 teeth.
22. M.A. = 8, V.R. = 8 ; M.A. = 5·6, V.R. = 8 ; Efficiency = 70%.
23. 38·4 lb. ; 48 lb. ; 80 lb. ; 112 lb. ; 144 lb
24. $22\frac{1}{2}$; 30 lb. ; 75% efficiency.
25. 20 r.p.m.
27. 0·182 in.
28. 11·4.
29. 140 lb.
30. 6.
31. 8·25 lb.
32. $E = \dfrac{W}{8} + \dfrac{3}{4}$
33. V.R. = 50 ; Efficiency = 0·48.

EXERCISE 7. Page 121

1. 132·8° F. ; 13·3° C.
2. 149° F. ; 45° C.
3. Thermometer reads 0·2° F. too low.
4. Substitute 45° F. and 50° F.
5. 60·8° F.
6. Thermometer reads 0·3° F. too low.
7. (a) 2912° F. ; (b) 10,832° F. ; (c) 98·6° F. ; (d) 674·6° F. ; (e) −38·02° F. ;
   (f) 172·4° F. ; (g) −173·2° F. ; (h) −41·8° F.
8. (a) 50° F. ; 158° F. ; 35·6° F.
   (b) −40° C. = −40° F.

EXERCISE 8. Page 132

1. 15·8° F.
2. 1150° C.
3. 0·64.
4. 835° C.
5. 0·274.
6. 0·35 ; 9·85 grams.
7. 0·41.
8. 20·2° C.
9. 0·486.
10. 1·78 pence.
11. 31·68 pence.
12. 16s. 10d.
13. 3520 calories ; 76·4° C.
14. 227·5 Therms ; £9 9s. 7d. ; 50,555 cub. ft.
15. (a) 12·32 C.H.U. ; (b) 8220 C.H.U. per lb.
16. 10,555½ C.H.U. ; 450 B.Th.U.
17. 210 C.H.U. ; 378 B.Th.U.
18. 13 C.H.U. ; (a) 14·44 C.H.U. ; (b) 7222 C.H.U. per lb.
19. 38·7° C.
20. 66° F.
21. 0·36.
22. 82·2° C.
23. 0·318.
24. 0·438.

EXERCISE 9. Page 140

1. 54·9° C.
2. 3,625,000 calories.
3. 539·3 calories per gram.
4. 485,000 lb.
5. 74·4%.
6. 266 lb.
7. 980 lb.
8. 13·4 lb.
9. 380 cub. ft. per hour.
10. 1,769,100 C.H.U.
11. 61·8° C. ; 98,500 C.H.U.
12. 7·55 lb.
13. Sensible heat 248,000 C.H.U. ;   Latent heat 964,000 C.H.U. :
    Total heat 1,212,000 C.H.U.
14. 139 min.
15. 1158 B.Th.U. ; 8·45 lb.
16. 220 C.H.U. ; 673 C.H.U. ; 7·65 lb.

EXERCISE 10. Page 149

1. 5·44 mm.
2. 30 cm. ; 30·214 cm.
3. 0·068 cm.
4. 1·65 in.
5. 0·016 in.
6. 3·64 in.
7. 12·8 in.
8. 17·28 thousandths.
9. 42·156 in.
10. 71·921 in. ; 353° C.
11. 0·0274 in.
12. 0·384 in.
13. 0·608 in.
14. 0·0000167.
15. 432° C.
16. 360·428 in.

EXERCISE 11. Page 154

1. 6·68 min.
2. 254·5 min.
3. 3,833,333 B.Th.U. ; 1,135,000 B.Th.U. ; 29·7%.
4. 58·8 h.p.
5. 6·38 h.p.
6. 0·68 gall. per hour.
7. 10·7 h.p. ; 5·25 lb. per hour.
8. 103 min.
9. 1070 min. ; 71·3 pence.
10. 8·85 h.p. ; 5·29 kilowatts.
11. 437,500 ft. tons.
12. 3530 C.H.U. per hour.
13. 17·2 min.
14. 31·7 watts.
15. 6·7 h.p. ; 4·31 lb. per hour.
16. 139 min.
17. 1,235,000,000 ft. lb. per min. ; 37,500 h.p.

EXERCISE 12. Page 168

1. 0·176 cub. ft.
2. Absolute pressures 45, 85, 115, 195 lb. per in.^{2}
   Gauge pressures 2, 12, 57, 80, 120 lb. per in.^{2}

3. 19·3 cub. ft. ; 41·5 cub. ft. ; 276·6 cub. ft.
4. 50·62 cub. ft. ; 101·25 lb./sq. in. abs.
5. 1·44 cub. ft.
6. 13·9 cub. ft.
7. 36·96 atmospheres.
8. 3020 c.c.
9. 316 cub. ft.
10. 2020 cub. ft. ; 163·5 lb.
11. 25 lb. per in.^{2}
12. 117·6 per in.^{2} ; 8·82 cub. ft.
13. 66·6 lb. per in.^{2} ; 44·4 lb. per in.^{2} ; 33·3 lb. per in.^{2}
14. 473° C.
15. 3430 cub. ft.
16. 34·2% increase.

INDEX

Fuel, calorific value of, 124.
Fulcrum, 92.

Gas, calorific value of, 124.
Gauge pressure, 137.
Gear wheel, 100.
Gravity, 3, 58.

Heat,
    effects of, 114.
    energy, 66.
    engine, 114.
    latent, 135.
    sensible, 135.
    specific, 126.
    total, 136.
    transference of, 128.
Hooke's law, 50.
Horsepower, 69, 153.

Ideal effort, 84.
    machine, 84.
Idler gear, 101.
Inclined plane, 13, 19, 21, 81, 96, 172
Isothermal expansion, 160.

Jib crane, 12, 17.
Joule, 152.

Kilowatt, 70, 153.
Kilowatt hour, 70.
Kinetic energy, 66.

Latent heat of fusion, 135.
    of vaporisation, 135.
Lathe drive, 105.
Law of machine, 85, 90.
Layout of experiment account, 171.
Lever, 91.
    bell-crank, 93.
    combination of, 94.
Limit of proportionality, 51.
Linear expansion, 143.
Load, 82.
Lubricant, 76.

Machines, 81.
    belt drive, 104.
    chain drive, 104.
    gear drive, 100.

Machines (cont.)
    inclined plane, 96.
    law of, 85, 90.
    lever, 91.
    perfect, 84.
    screw-jack, 98.
    wheel and axle, 95.
    winch, 102.
Mid-ordinates, 62.
Mixtures, heat transference in, 128
Modulus of elasticity, 50.
Moment of force, 34, 35.
Moments, principle of, 36.

Perfect machine, 85.
Permanent set, 52.
Plane, inclined, 13, 19, 21, 81, 96, 172
Potential energy, 66
Power, 68.
    electrical, 70, 153.
Principle of conservation of energy, 68
    of moments, 36.
Pyrometer, 116.

Quantity of heat, 123.

Rate of work, 68.
Reaction of beam supports, 41
    forces, 12.
Resolution of forces, 26.
Resultant force, 5, 7.
Rockets, 151.

Safety, factor of, 53.
Saturation temperature, 135.
Screw-jack, 98.
Seizure of bearings, 151.
Sensible heat, 135.
Simpson's rule, 62.
Smooth surface, 13, 19.
Space diagram, 4.
Specific heat, 126.
Spring extension, 49.
Spur gearing, 100.
Strain, 48.
Strength, ultimate tensile, 53.
Stress, 48.
    allowable working, 53.
Style of writing, 172.
Superficial expansion, 143.